WOMEN ARE WONDERFUL!

A HISTORY IN CARTOONS

OF A HUNDRED YEARS

WITH AMERICA'S MOST CONTROVERSIAL FIGURE

EDITED BY

WILLIAM COLE AND FLORETT ROBINSON

HOUGHTON MIFFLIN COMPANY · BOSTON

The Riverside Press · Cambridge   1956

The Riverside Press
CAMBRIDGE • MASSACHUSETTS
PRINTED IN THE U. S. A.

TABLE OF CONTENTS

INTRODUCTION

THIS IS a lighthearted history. It looks back a hundred years and then brings us up to the American woman as she is today — her bustle behind her, her corset shucked, separate from, but equal to the male. Through all these years the American cartoonist has wittily, and unwittingly, made a graphic record of the immense change that has taken place in her status. Much of the advance is due to her own efforts to climb down off the Victorian pedestal where man had placed her; other changes came about through the natural flow of history.

It would be hard to say which has changed more in the past century, the American woman or the American cartoon. The basic woman, of course, hasn't changed since Eve, and never will. But from Plymouth Rock to the Civil War the prevailing male attitude went along with Shakespeare's "Frailty, thy name is woman!" In 1848 a group of American women, dissatisfied with being treated as housekeepers and hothouse plants, held the first *Woman's Rights* meeting in Seneca Falls, New York. The males thought this was pretty funny; they indulged the fair sex, and secretly they guffawed. But the meeting was a success, and led to further meetings and further organization under the guidance of such unfrail creatures as *Elizabeth Cady Stanton, Susan B. Anthony, Carrie Chapman Catt,* and *Belva Lockwood* — a woman who twice ran for President of the United States in the eighties. The women were militant; they were cajoling. They wrote and they spoke and they pulled together, and gradually, over the years, they won their fights for woman suffrage, for sensible clothing, for education, and for freedom from the restrictions that a masculine society had placed upon them in social, business, and professional life.

Coincidentally with the first stirrings of organized discontent from the women, the first examples of comic art began to appear in such family magazines as *Harper's Bazar* (now *Bazaar*) and *Harper's Weekly,* and in such early humor magazines as *Vanity Fair* and *Yankee Notions.* The drawing for the most part was crude, the captions long and labored. Speaking of the cartoons of this period, the authority on prints, *Frank Weitenkampf,* has written: "When our social life had so developed that material was found for criticism and satire, it was the crudities of the male, relic of a pioneer age, that got the pictorial slap. But soon woman came in for her share, particularly on account of her social aspirations, adherences to fashion in dress to any extent of vagary, and striving for more political and social rights." And through the years since that time the American cartoonists, predominantly male (and some of them perhaps jealous of women elbowing into *their* world), have had a go at contemporary female fashions and follies. "The New Woman" was depicted as losing her precious femininity by smoking, drinking, and wearing trousers in public. She was shown in assiduous pursuit of the shy male, and then, once she had nabbed him, she was pictured leaving him at home to baby-sit while she flounced out to Woman's Rights assemblages.

The first flowering of the cartoon-as-a-work-of-art came in the 1870s, when the two great figures were the crusading *Thomas Nast* of *Harper's Weekly,* most of whose cartoons were political, and *Joseph Keppler,* also at times a political crusader, who founded the humorous weekly, *Puck,* in 1877. Keppler had come to America from Vienna in 1868, and after a period in St. Louis had gravitated to New York where he established a German-language *Puck* in 1876 which ran for many years side by side with the English version. He was a master of graphic satire, and *Puck* launched a new era in American humor. *Judge* Magazine founded in 1881, was also political, but it was primarily a weekly of high-spirited, low-down humor. In 1883 the humor magazine *Life* entered the scene in a dignfied manner. *Life* from which we have drawn more heavily than any other publication for this book, was modeled on the English *Punch*: it was a snob-appeal magazine, refined and genteel, for the "right people." Its cartoons poked respectful fun at what these right people were doing, what they were wearing, and where they were being seen. America, which felt a bit rough around the social edges, welcomed some guidance to the fashionable world, and *Life* prospered.

Life's star contributor every week from the 1890s and on, for some thirty years, was *Charles Dana Gibson,* master of elegance in drawing and creator of that idealized American female "The Gibson Girl." At the same time that *Life* was featuring Gibson and the beautifully flowing line of *Otho Cushing, Puck* had three top cartoonists of its own who specialized in the foibles of fashionable women: *Samuel D. Ehrhart* caught the ruffles and roguishness of well-bred young ladies of the period; *Frank A. Nankivell* created pert and curvaceous young things who could vie with any glamour girl of today, and, in the 1880s, *C. J. Taylor* had a smartly turned out society belle, "The Taylor Made Girl" — a precourser of the Gibson Girl.

In the cartoons of the nineties, and up to the first World War, one finds long, involved captions which identify everyone in the drawing thoroughly, and often give stage directions as well. A caption would begin: NEW YORKER *(who has been "stuck" more than an hour with intellectual young lady from Boston),* and go on discoursively for three or four lines. The names of the actors in a situation were also part of the joke: "Mrs. De Korator" who has gilded her rolling pin and hung it up as a parlor decoration, and "Mrs. Hunnimune," whose name is self-explanatory. The change from the long-drawn-out "He and She" caption to the direct impact one-liner (or for that matter, to no caption at all) that we find today was gradual. The one-line caption didn't start with *The New Yorker,* as is popularly believed; they did of course, bring it to the peak of perfection. Examples of single line captions may be found in *Thomas Craven's* fascinating book *"Cartoon Cavalcade"* from as early as 1899, and in the work of *Art Young,* before World War I, the cartoon itself can be seen brought to a high degree of simplicity and directness.

The four great cartoonists who best represent, in style and content, a capsule history of humorous drawing in America are *Thomas Nast, Charles Dana Gibson, John Held, Jr.,* and *Peter Arno.* Held's work first began to attract attention in *Judge* about 1913. He then moved over to *Life,* where he became *the* cartoonist of the Jazz Age — flappers and sugar daddies, tenor saxophones and bathtub gin. When *The New Yorker* came on the scene in 1925, many of the cartoonists who had been working for *Life* and *Judge,* including Held, either moved over to it completely, or worked three sides of the street, doing a bit for each of the magazines. Among these artists were *Gardner Rea, Ralph Barton, Al Frueh, Rea Irvin,* and a supersophisticated newcomer, *Peter Arno.* Arno's cartoons are the work of a perfectionist; a master who knows what effect he wishes to make, and the most direct way of making it. He is *The New Yorker* cartoonist *par excellence,* and has influenced the magazine and his fellow cartoonists tremendously.

Puck faded away during World War I, in 1918. *Life* and *Judge,* after long and painful declines, gave up in the 1930s. Since then, *The New Yorker* has been the undisputed and unchallenged champion in the cartoon field.

The first woman to break through into the masculine work of cartoonists was *O'Neill Latham,* whose rich black and white drawings appeared in the humor magazines of the nineties and early nineteen hundreds. Another pioneer of that period was *Rose O'Neill,* the inventor of kewpies, who was married to the humorist Harry Leon Wilson. Since the 1930's there have been many fine women cartoonists, the most noted being *Mary Petty,* delineator of thin-blooded aristocrats and their servants, and, of course, the great *Helen Hokinson,* whose special bailiwick was the woman's clubs of suburbia.

In his definitive book *A History of American Graphic Humor, William Murrell* writes, "Of all the artists the cartoonist is closest to the people, and in America he is, almost without exception, one of them." This is particularly true of those men who represent the great age of the newspaper cartoonist — an age which is almost over. There was *Clare Briggs* with his "Mr. and Mrs." series, which suffered a decline when someone else took it over after his death in 1930; *H. T.*

Webster's "Timid Soul" and bridge cartoons, which also fell in quality when the creator died; *Denys Wortman's* heartwarming "Metropolitan Movies", *Fontaine Fox's* late-lamented Toonerville folks, and, happily still appearing after two or three decades, *W. E. Hill's* perceptive Sunday pages on suburbanites and city dwellers, and *J. R. Williams's* "Out Our Way" family, and his factory workers and cowboys. Along with the contributors to *Puck, Judge, Life* and *The New Yorker,* these are the movers and shakers, the great cartoonists of America.

We believe that in this book we have examples of the best in American cartooning. In a few cases, unfortunately, there was nothing that had to do specifically with women to be found — *George Harrimann's* "Krazy Kat" and *Walt Kelly's* "Pogo" didn't offer anything quite in our line, and the newspaper cartoons of *T. A. Dorgan* — "Tad's Indoor Sports" — deal mainly with masculine situations.

While we have been thorough in our coverage of cartoonists, we admit that to represent the American woman, in all her infinite variety, would take twenty volumes such as this. So we have shown only the high spots of her progress and personality. If it should appear that these cartoons dwell more on her absurdities than on her virtues, that is unavoidable, since humor is basically a matter of exaggeration and incongruity. Our tribute to the American woman is from the heart by way of the funnybone.

About two years ago, when the feminine half of this editorial team brought up the idea for a graphic tribute to her sex, the prospect looked fairly simple — a matter of plucking the finest flowers of American cartooning from here and there and weaving them into a garland. As it turned out, alas, there were many thorns to the garland. Going through the back volumes of forty years of a weekly magazine can become soporific, and there are many such magazines; and the lifetime output of a daily newspaper cartoonist adds up to a staggering number of cartoons. Then there was research in the history of the American cartoon, and the history of women; also the problem of getting reproducible copies of cartoons, and much correspondence. However, as you can see, a book came out of it. Our thanks are due to the splendid cooperation of the cartoonists and their agents. We are also grateful to the amazingly efficient staff of the New York Public Library, where most of the research was done; to Miss Ramona Javitz, Curator of the Picture Collection, and her staff; to Miss Elizabeth Roth and Mr. Wilson G. Duprey of the Print Room, and to the members of the Photographic Services who handled the large volume of material with courtesy and dispatch.

And last our most specific thanks go to Houghton Mifflin's airborne editor, John Leggett, whose motto could be "Ready, Willing, and Able."

July, 1956   WILLIAM COLE and FLORETT ROBINSON

FASHION
AND
BEAUTY

THE ABSURDITIES AND VAGARIES OF CLOTHING AND COSMETICS
FROM HOOP SKIRTS TO HARDLY ANY, FROM THE OVERSTUFFED
TO THE UNDERDRESSED, FROM THE POMPADOUR TO THE BOB
TO THE POODLE CUT.

POLICE CONSTABLE (to boy): "Now, then, off with that hoop, or I'll precious soon help you!"
LADY (who imagines the observation is addressed to her): "What a monster! [Lifts up the crinoline, and hurries off]

Three cartoons from the hoop skirt era, from three representative magazines: a daring *double entendre* from an 1857 *Harper's Weekly* (above), and comments from *Yankee Notions* in 1861 (below, left) and *Vanity Fair* in 1862 (below, right).

A VOYAGE THROUGH BROADWAY

We wouldn't for the world say anything derogatory to the fair sex; but we appeal to any unprejudiced person to say whether the above is not a nuisance.

A DELICATE POSITION ALL ROUN

TRULY SO!

SWEET MARY ANN: *"Husband, I wish you would buy me some pretty feathers."*
MARY ANN'S "OWN": *"Indeed, my dear little wife, you look better without them."*
SWEET M. A.: *"Oh, no, sir; you always call me your little bird, and how does a bird look without feathers?"*

LADIES TAKE NOTE

MISS JONES: *"Don't you see! I'm getting myself up 'Iron Clad' for the bathing season! In these war times nothing's safe unless iron clad."*

Not exactly our idea of a hilarious caption (above, left) but a fine glimpse of a lady's foundations in 1862. The Civil War battle of the *Monitor* and the *Merrimac* inspired a jab at female fashion (above, right) in the same year. The pony-tail hair-do (below, right) as shown in 1865, was to make a reappearance in fashion almost a hundred years later.

FASHIONABLE EXTREMES

l Accident to Mrs. Flimsey's Waterfall, Through Fashionable Taste of a Misguided Horse.

"Imitation is the sincerest flattery."

WHY NOT?

C. S. Reinhart pokes fun at the off-the-shoulder dresses of 1872 in *Harper's Bazar*. A *Puck* cartoon about the long trains of the late 70's (below, left) and an uncanny bit of prophecy (below, right) from 1869.

PUCK VENTURES A MERE SUGGESTION

Utilize the long trains of fashionable mothers — à la kangaroo.

LE "FOLLY."

They say that long eye-lashes are to come in next season; but are they to be stuck on like chignons?

THE VERY LATEST INVENTION
THE ANTI-HUGGING STEEL CORSET FOR USE AT
CAMP MEETINGS.

BEAUTIFUL FOREVER (?)
MRS. MODE: "Good gracious! Hodson, do you mean to say that there's no more 'Arabian Enamel' to be obtained? Why, I'm positively cracking all over!"
HODSON (improving the occasion): "So you are, ma'am! And what's worse, it's beginning to chip off!"

Camp meetings, a heady combination of religious fervor and romance, kept the American scene lively in the nineteenth century and provoked the ingenious suggestion (top left). Somewhat grisly is the cartoon (top right) with its reminder that beauty was once only enamel-deep. Upon the occasion of Oscar Wilde's visit to New York, the sunflower, his symbol of the aesthetic cult, inspired the charming fantasy (lower left) by E. W. Kemble, including the fashionable bulldog.

THAT FASHIONABLE HAT

SUGGESTIONS FOR AN
AESTHETIC COSTUME.

1. As it was recently worn

2. When the style was changed

3. "All the rage" — as the wife of your bosom observes

4. What you may expect next winter

THE HAT OF THE FUTURE

FROM DESIGNS BY OUR SPECIAL FASHION ARTIST IN PARIS

From 1877, by Joseph Keppler, founder of *Puck*.

THE NEW STYLE OF CRINOLINE

A man has to use a compass to tell whether his wife is going backward or forward.

THE CHICAGO CRAZE

Every Garden City belle wants to have her hair cut like a little man's.

The *Police Gazette* (left) records what was fortunately only a passing fad of the 1880's. Bustles interfered with sidewalk traffic, just as the hoopskirt had done twenty-five years earlier.

A HINT TO THE MAYOR

When it comes to sidewalk obstruction why is not upper Broadway a good field for reform?

A handsome display in a low-cut bodice was a prerequisite of the fashionable lady of the 80's, and here C. J. Taylor, artist of high society, shows us an example in all its full-blown beauty. Below, there was danger for the male in even such a passing fad as the long veil.

A MODEST COVERING

WIFE: "Are my shoulders covered enough to suit you, dear?"
HUSBAND: "Not at all, my love; there is a spot as large as a dollar on your right shoulder without a speck of powder on it!"

THE VEIL TRICK — IN THREE ACTS

*Fashion produces a certain uniformity in the street
that is less noticeable . . .*

at the seashore.

A comment by C. J. Taylor (left) showing
that the bathing costumes of the nineties
were less revealing than evening costumes.
Another bathing suit joke by Hy Mayer,
popular cartoonist of the time, shows how
fashion can make or break a woman's
beauty.

HER FIRST PARTY SINCE THE SUMMER SEASON

*MISS BARHAVEN: "No, Papa, I'm not tattooed. It's the
effect of that high-necked bathing dress. You would insist on
my wearing it, you know."*

Not long ago, the men used to flock to the beach:

Bicycling fashions also had their allure in 1895, as they would today.

but now they seek sections of the country where the roads are good.

TIME WORKS MANY CHANGES

*A FAMILY LIABILITY IN THE BUXOM NINETIES —
THE DAUGHTER WHO IS TOO SLENDER EVER TO
BE STYLISH.*

Two cartoons from R. V. Cutler's series "The Gay Nineties," which appeared in *Life* in the late 1920's.

*IN THE "YOU-JUST-KNOW-SHE-WEARS-'EM" NINE-
TIES THE GALLANT LOVER HAD TO FIGHT COLD
STEEL TO WIN HIS LADY FAIR.*

VERSATILITY

CLARA: *"Why, Fanny, what sort of a bathing suit do you call that? What are all those buttons for?"*

FANNY: *"I'll show you. You know that one part of the season we spend at Ocean Grove — — and the other part at the Pier."*

HIGH-PRESSURE HAIR DRESSING

The novel and ingenious device by which a Long Branch bath-house attendant has made a handsome provision against a rainy day.

Ingenious devices, above and lower left made life interesting at the fashionable beaches around the turn of the century.

A CRITICISM

FAIR BATHER: *"Mrs. Weeds dresses that daughter of hers outrageously! She is seventeen if she is a day, and just see what short skirts she has on!"*

SECOND FAIR BATHER: *"Outrageous!"*

VIRTUE'S DEFENCE & THE HAT PIN
BY JOHN HELD JR. AS HE CHOKES BACK HIS TRUE FEELINGS

One of a series (left) of John Held, Jr., woodcuts on the Gay Nineties that appeared much later in *The New Yorker*. Two comments (below) on fashion idiosyncrasies by Samuel D. Ehrhart. The dust-catching skirt of that period inspired this grim warning (below, left) and the balloon sleeve drew a gibe by the same artist.

THE TRAILING SKIRT — DEATH LOVES A SHINING MARK.

AS FAR AS CONVENIENT

MRS. DE STYLE: *"I hear that puffed elbows are going out."*
MR. DE STYLE: *"Good Heavens! Aren't they out far enough already?"*

THE ENVY OF THE ALLEY
An Easter hat and a bunch of violets.

M. A. Woolf (above) touchingly portrayed the slum children of the nineties in his book *Sketches from Lowly Life,* and (below) J. R. Williams looks back at a fashion problem frequently met with in large families of the era.

THE EVOLUTION OF THE PUFF

THE LOST HUSBAND — WHICH ONE IS HIS WIFE?

Some views of the huge hats of 1908-09. Gordon Grant (top) was a frequent contributor to *Puck*. He was also known as an artist of the sea.

SOLVED!

PREACHER: "On this beautiful Easter morn, let us resolve to have a broader vision."
SMALL VOICE: "Amen!"

WHILE THE CARRIAGE WAITS

TUBE BE OR NOT TUBE BE?

A fashionable pun by Gordon Grant, and an amusing drawing by Orson Lowell, showing two of the difficulties of the mode in 1909.

LE MINARET

"It certainly is fierce, Mrs. Simmons; but if them jokers in Parus says it's the thing, we'll hev to come to it, and that's all there is to that."

THEY HAVEN'T WORN THEM YET

But give them time: they will.

LOCOMOTION
and the close-fitting skirt

A CRITERION

MRS. MODE: "But, monsieur, I really couldn't wear this gown — it's indecent!"

MONS. WURTH: "Nowadays, madam, nothing is indecent but to show the tips of one's ears."

The silhouette changed, and dresses became more revealing from 1913 on, as shown in these cartoons from *Judge*.

narkable change a few years have made in Mrs. Jone's shape.

A SUGGESTION

MAID: "It's awful cold tonight, ma'am. Hadn't you better wear the muff and carry the dress?"

WHY NOT MAKE THE FASHIONS CHARACTERISTIC OF THE WEARER?

There was a tendency toward the mannish (below) in sports clothes for the ladies in 1913.

SUMMER GIRLS AND SOME'RE NOT

John Held, Jr. (right), who was to be *the* recorder of the short-skirt era, appeared in *Life* in 1917 with this glimpse of the future. By 1920 the cartoonists, including James Montgomery Flagg (below, left), were really beginning to be alarmed by the ascent of the skirt. But they hadn't seen anything yet.

THOSE SHORT SKIRTS

BUTLER: *"Miss Van Smythe asks, sir, if you will step in the next room, as she wishes to come down stairs."*

ALMOST SUCCESSFUL

A young girl both simple and sweet,
When asked was her costume complete,
*   Said, "It really is hell,*
*   This H. C. of L.*
I'm striving to make both ends meet!"

TAKE NO CHANCES

EMINENT PHYSICIAN: *"As we have no idea what the fashions may be when your daughter grows up, I think it wise to vaccinate her on the tongue."*

GIRTH CONTROL

By Orson Lowell, witty caricaturist of the social life of the pre-World War I era.

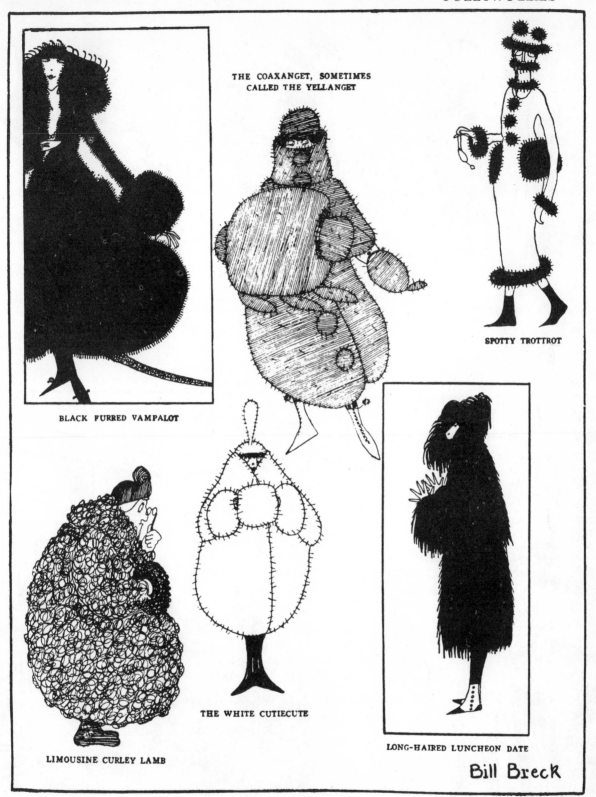

THE COAXANGET, SOMETIMES
CALLED THE YELLANGET

SPOTTY TROTTROT

BLACK FURRED VAMPALOT

THE WHITE CUTIECUTE

LIMOUSINE CURLEY LAMB

LONG-HAIRED LUNCHEON DATE

Bill Breck

ANIMALS OF NORTH AMERICAN CITIES

HOW TO RECOGNIZE THE FURRY TRIBE

With the war over, fashion returned as a major interest, and the ladies burst out in an amazing variety of luxurious furs.

1898
Poor slave lacing wife's corset.

1908
Same serf buttoning wife's waist.

1923
The slipover dress.

Three fine cartoonists of the early twenties comment on fashion. Paul Reilly (above), Don Herold (below, left), and Ellison Hoover (below, right) in one of a series that ran in *Life*.

A WOMAN'S IDEA OF A PERFECT
POCKETBOOK

INTIMATE GLIMPSES OF AMERICAN GENERA
OF INDUSTRY
The Seventh Sutherland Sister Bobs Her Hair

THE VERY LATEST CONCEIT FROM LONDON: THE
PNEUMATIC RIDING BREECHES

THE NEW CHINTZ KNICKERBOCKER
IN WHICH A GIRL LOOKS WORSE
THAN IN THE KHAKI ONE (IF
THAT IS POSSIBLE)

PARIS DECREES:
Fashions Will Be Louder
and Funnier

IT IS PREDICTED THAT A GREAT
MANY PETTISKIRTS WILL BE SEEN
AT THE SMARTER PLACES

THE OVERHEAD WAISTLINE,
VERY *chic*

THE ANKLE WAISTLINE—EVEN A
BIT *chicer*

IN THIS DESIGN YOU HAVE YOUR
CHOICE OF THE LOCATION

John Held, Jr., has some fun with the fashions of 1924.

. . . . . *AND SHORTER*

"Fifty years ago, Elizabeth, I preached against trousers for women.
Now I'm praying God will send them quick . . . before it's too late."

Three cartoons about the short skirts and boyish figures of the late 20's by J. Conacher (above), J. Norman Lynd (below, left), and, with a very famous caption, John Held, Jr. (below, right).

IN SOME CASES IT'S HARD
TO TELL WHETHER THEY'RE
BOYS OR GIRLS — EXCEPT
BY THE EARRINGS

URSULA: *"Is my nose shiny, Dearie?"*
LAMBERT: *"No, but your right knee is dusty."*

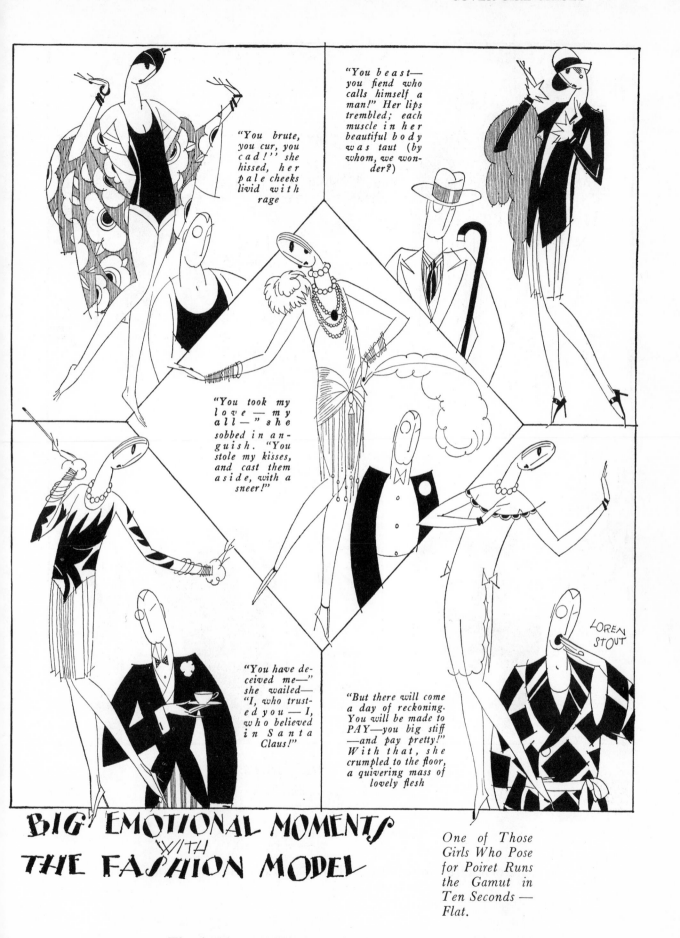

"You brute, you cur, you cad!" she hissed, her pale cheeks livid with rage

"You beast— you fiend who calls himself a man!" Her lips trembled; each muscle in her beautiful body was taut (by whom, we wonder?)

"You took my love — my all—" she sobbed in anguish. "You stole my kisses, and cast them aside, with a sneer!"

"You have deceived me—" she wailed— "I, who trusted you — I, who believed in Santa Claus!"

"But there will come a day of reckoning. You will be made to PAY—you big stiff —and pay pretty!" With that, she crumpled to the floor, a quivering mass of lovely flesh

LOREN STOUT

BIG EMOTIONAL MOMENTS WITH THE FASHION MODEL

One of Those Girls Who Pose for Poiret Runs the Gamut in Ten Seconds — Flat.

The fashion models haven't changed since 1927, as Loren Stout shows us, although the fashions have.

SHALL WE APE THE LADIES?

A delightful fantasy by Al Frueh on fashion inanities of 1925.

BRINGING UP FATHER

"My dear, your skirt is positively
dragging!"

Emancipated Woman

When the stock market fell, it seems that skirts fell, too. Things weren't bad enough for the American men — now *this* had to happen! Cartoonist Kemp Starrett gets back at the French fashion designers who set this unpopular style (left).

HUBBY: *"Guess what I have in my hand for you!"*

WIFIE: *"I bet it's new undies!"*

HUBBY: *"Yes, but how many?"*

Gaar Williams (below, right) reminds us of the reducing craze of the early thirties, when pounds were taken off to the rhythm of band music on the radio.

How shall I make my eyebrows today, Doris —
ke Marlene Dietrich's, Constance Bennett's or
nita Page's?"

MORNING CALL

PANTS PRESSED WHILE YOU WAIT

OLD LADIES' HOME

CASTOFFS

HERE COMES THE BRIDE

"HA, HA, HA, — THEY'RE MY SISTER'S!!"

TWO PANTS SUIT

APRIL FOOL

"M'LADY'S PANTS"

Slacks were all the rage in 1933,
Reamer Keller shows us (left), a
there was a brief run on beach p
jamas (below), these particular or
put on exhibit by J. Norman Lynd.

THE MODE IS
BEACH PYJAMAS, BUT
THERE ARE STILL OLD-FASHIONED
GIRLS WHO EXPOSE THE KNEES

FASCINATING

"For God's sake, quick, Miss Tyndale, thin it out with water!"

Even in Boston, men were (and are) driven mad by women's artificial lures, as recorded by Dahl of the *Boston Herald-Traveler* (above) and by the *Harvard Lampoon* (left).

"*I thought Mother asked you not to do that!*"

The great cartoonist Sam Cobean shows us the dangers of décolleté (above), and (below, right) a college humor magazine, the *California Pelican,* comments on another danger peculiar to our time.

"*Just give me an honest opinion on how it looks bearing in mind, of course, that I don't have my hair up or the proper accessories on.*"

A defense of local loveliness by Dahl of Boston (above), and a reminder by Henry
Syverson that styles have changed considerably in thirty years.

"Mabel Benson! *Where've you
been keeping yourself?*"

The post-war mode brought some oddities: the man's-shirt-and-blue-jeans combination (left), the bikini bathing suit, and the gamin haircut.

"Your eyes are like stars, your lips are clare wine . . . your hair . . . er . . . you have a beau tifully shaped head."

A slender figure has always been a matter of great concern to women. Saul Steinberg's ladies (above) hide what defects they may have under voluminous furs. The *Harvard Lampoon* lampoons corset ads (below, right), and Chon Day makes a comment (below, left) that would turn a man's blood cold.

Good-by steam baths, good-by slenderizing eatments, good-by low-calorie diets."

"I'd like to see something that lifts and moulds the body to bring out its youthful lines and yet does not destroy the natural grace of the mature figure."

38

"But I can't!"

WHITHER ARE WE DRIFTING?

TOONERVILLE FOLKS

The widely syndicated Fontaine Fox shows the male reaction to *any* change in fashion (above).

"We didn't dress like this in my day."

HIGH FASHION

Theatrical caricaturist Al Hirschfeld indicates that where fashion is concerned, there is a man behind every woman.

LOVE, SEX, AND THE PURSUIT OF THE MALE

THE OBJECT HAS ALWAYS BEEN THE SAME: A MAN, BUT THE
METHODS AND PROBLEMS OF PURSUIT HAVE VARIED.
CHAPERONS AND DOLLAR PRINCESSES; SPARKING, PETTING,
AND NECKING; POST OFFICE AND MORE DIRECT FEMININE LURES.

AN IMPOSSIBLE ORDER TO OBEY

OFFICER: *"Attention! Can't you hear! Eyes to the front! Right dress! Why can't you obey!"*

That eternal lure, the well-turned ankle, had its effect on the boys in blue in 1862 (above) and the war itself was used as bait to catch a man (below). Both cartoons from *Yankee Notions.*

COOL

KATE: *"They draft the single men first, Charlie."*
CHARLIE: *"Yes, I think they do, Kate. Why?"*
KATE: *"Nothing, only I was thinking how you could avoid the draft — that's all."*

GRAND CHARGE OF LADIES IN LEAP YEAR

AFTER THE BATTLE — LEADING AWAY THE CAPTIVES

The fine old institution of Leap Year enabled modest maidens to take the offensive one day annually (above). If a suitor was particularly laggard (right), Papa sometimes hurried things along. Both cartoons from *Harper's Bazar*, 1872.

A MATRIMONIAL REMINDER

THE FATHER: "Mr. Johnson, for two years you have been 'Keeping Company.' Suppose you begin 'Keeping House'?"

BOTH SIDES OF A QUESTION

ELIGIBLE BACHELOR (to host): "Marry, indeed! Do you think any sensible man would marry a girl with such a waist as that one upstairs?"

THAT GIRL UPSTAIRS (to hostess): "Ye it is very silly and my waist is terribly unco fortable, but I suppose I shall have to do it u til I am married."

THE HAMMOCK

A gibe at the "Wedding Ring" waist (above), and a tribute (below) to a celebrated aid to courtship.

Seven P.M.

Eight P.M.

Nine P.M.

In the 1890's the cartoon began to be more a cartoon and less an illustration; witness the work of F. M. Howarth.

IN LEAP YEAR

The Reluctant Men are Coaxed into the Breakers

THE BEAR AND THE SUMMER GIRL; OR

A Charles Dana Gibson summer extravaganza from 1892 (left), and (below) a cartoon tribute to the efficacy of a kiss, by O. W. Simons.

PRACTICE MAKES PERFECT

OUR AMERICAN GIRLS ARE CAPTURING THE
HOUSE OF LORDS

A Sure Guarantee of Peace Between America and England

This cartoon, by C. J. Taylor, is one of many pictorial comments that appeared in the American press from 1890 to 1915 on the "Dollar Princesses" — wealthy American girls who went to Europe in search of titles. The social stamp of approval on duke-hunting came when Consuelo Vanderbilt married the Duke of Marlborough in 1895, the year the above cartoon appeared in *Puck*.

A comment (above) on the Dollar Princesses from a German magazine in 1908. The caption reads: "There goes an heiress toward Dollarland leading a camel by a halter." Some girls of the period, however, seem to have stuck to the pursuit of their own compatriots (below) when abroad.

FROM OVER THE SEA

MISS M.: "Is the American mail in?"
CLERK: "Yes, miss; he is in room 56."

"Why did you kiss me?"
"Well, I heard you were a woman with a past, and I thought I would give you a little present."

A mild romantic jest, above, but a drawing of extreme sophistication in the *fin de siècle* manner by Otho Cushing. Right, a catty comment accompanied by an elegant drawing, this time by stylist Frank A. Nankivell.

IMPUTATION

EDITH: *"See the solitaire ring Harold gave me! What think of the stone?"*
ETHEL: *"Very pretty! What do you suppose it is?"*

O'Neill Latham, one of the earliest woman cartoonists (left) shows mother explaining the ways of a man with a maid to her innocent daughter. If she doesn't learn her lesson she may end up as Samuel D. Ehrhart's old maid (below) — a stock funny character in those days.

THE REGULATION PROPOSAL

DAUGHTER: "No, Mama, Harold has not proposed as yet; that is, not in so many words."
MOTHER: "Mercy me, Jane! You must not wait for words! Proposals are mostly made up of sighs, gurgles, stammers, coughs, hems, haws, and looks, you know!"

SHE COULDN'T SAY

MABEL: "Is that a realistic love story, Aunty?"
MAIDEN AUNT (sighing): "Ah! How I wish I knew, child!"

J. R. Williams (above) tak[es]
backward glance at the sho[ck]
effect Post Office could have [on a]
shy young thing, and (left) I[....]
Glackens reminds us of the [ever-]
present chaperon.

AT THE HOTEL HOP

SUMMER GIRL: "Auntie, do sit down! Everybody is looking
at us. You don't have to chaperon me when I'm dancing."

Two journeys back into nostalgia by the great newspaper cartoonist Clare Briggs.

STRANGE, INDEED

MINERVA: "Isn't it strange, Mother, that all the
heroines in novels marry poor men?"
MATER: "Yes, my dear; but that is fiction."

Two period pieces from 1917. In the silhouette cartoon below we have the glamour
boy of the time — the Arrow Collar man.

JACK: "Was it you I kissed last night on the
veranda?"
JILL: "Let me see—about what time was it?"

Two flapper cartoons of the twenties, by John Held, Jr. (left), and Garrett Price (below). The extreme frankness of that era is revealed in both the caption and the setting of Mr. Price's cartoon.

SHE: "And I'm not really happy unless I have a man to dominate me."

MAUDE: "The boy I'm going with now thinks of nothing but necking."
CLAIRE: What can you do with a fellow like that?"
MAUDE: "Neck."

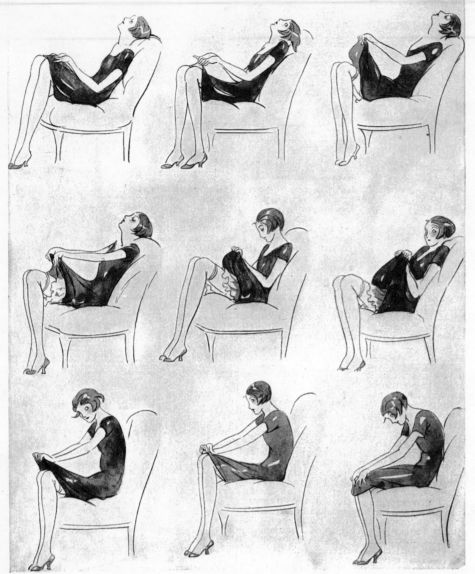

Slow-Motion Picture of a Young Lady Adjusting Her Skirt

The girl of the twenties pursu
male by leg, hip, and fist.
Herford gives us a sly flapper
and J. Norman Lynd (belov
shows us another approac
popular cartoonist Marge (
shows us that the girl of the
preserved *some* modesty.

A SHIVERY WIGGLE HAS
GOT A GOOD HOME FOR
MANY A GIRL

*"Yoo hoo, girls! Freddie gave me
fraternity pin!"*

"I'm putting in a couple extra sandwiches. Maybe you'll meet a nice fella at the beach."

Denys Wortman's New York girls pursue the male at the beach (with mother's blessing and aid) and the dance hall.

"As soon as I seen you on the floor I says: Thet's the girl I'm gonna take home tonight."

"So you think I buy dames malteds for nothing!"

The children of the thirties, as exemplifie
by William Steig's small fry, had a health
and forthright approach to the facts of life

"All he wanted was my body."

"She's had twelve proposals so far this fall, — all indecent."

Whitney Darrow, Jr. (above), shows that the pride of motherhood can go to any lengths, and George Price (below) comments on the necessarily quick marriages of World War II.

"Mrs. Newcomb takes care of furlough brides."

"I'm trying to warn you about men, Alicia — stop screaming 'How wonderful!'"

"Sorry, man, this isn't Hot Lips. It's Daddy-O."

"Oh, my soul's own idol! How shall I describe the feeling of your golden locks upon my brow . . . the touch of your gently curling eyelashes against my cheek . . . your beautifully classic profile reflected in the orbicular pools of your lambent eyes . . . throat of Carrara marble . . . that guileless look of a Goddess . . . the purity of your chaste complexion . . ."

"What I can't get across to him is that I'm not the intellectual type all the time."

"Stop following me around!"

Fourteen

Fifteen

Sixteen

Seventeen

Eighteen

Nineteen

"Stop following me around!"

She has a way with men

Abner Dean, above, on the happy ability s
women have to inflate the male ego,
Cobean, left, showing that when she's a
with her dreams, the American woman w
to be the pursued, not the pursuer.

SPORTS

FROM THE GENTEEL ACTION OF CROQUET AND THE BICYCLE-
BUILT-FOR-TWO TO THE MORE STRENUOUS ACTIVITIES OF
SOFTBALL TEAMS AND LADY WRESTLERS.

Mr. B., from Old England, having taken the girls up to Central Park to show 'em how to skate, is rather surprised at finding himself left in the background by feminine fast New York.

Before the Civil War it was unheard of for women to actively participate in sports, except for a bit of ice skating, which they apparently did with some spirit, according to the above cartoon from *Vanity Fair* in 1860. *Puck,* below, shows us that things were also lively out at Coney Island in the 1870's.

CONEY ISLAND

This · young · lady · feels · confident · that ·
Her · lawn · tennis · reduces · her · fat ·
But · she · always · will · play
In · a · violent · way
And · she · knocks · what · she · hits · very · flat ·

Tennis became a popular sport for women in the 1870's, as A. B. Frost notes on the left. Below we have a bit of prognostication from 1887.

NEW YORK AGAINST BOSTON FOR THE CHAMPIONSHIP

AN IMPORTANT POINT

"I'm afraid we are a little slow yet."
"Possibly: but I'm sure we don't look slow!"

Two cartoonists of the nineties, Frank A. Nankivell, above, and C. J. Taylor, below, indicate that with the fair sex form has always been extremely important in sport.

FORCE OF HABIT

LAURA: "The riding is lovely; but —"
REGGIE: "But what?"
LAURA: "Am I on the horse straight?"

On the left Nankivell elegantly records the craze for coaching among the well-to-do in 1900. F. Opper, below, shows that the romantic bicycle built-for-two could sometimes change into a domestic treadmill.

A WHISPER IN THE REAR

RS. NEWROCKS: *"Why, a few years ago I wouldn't ve dreamed of this!"*
ISS NEWROCKS: *"Never mind, Mama! Even if you n't feel blasé you should try to look blasé."*

A DREAM AND THE AWAKENING

MR. SPROCKETS *(during his courtship):* *"Ah, Miss Handlebarr, how sweet it would be to go through life together thus! I would never weary with your fairy form always before me!"*

MR. SPROCKETS *(two years after marriage):* *"I tell you what it is, Julia, at the rate you're gaining flesh, we'll have to get separate wheels right away, or I'll be a broken-down man!"*

UNPROFESSIONAL SUDDENNESS

MISS BUNKER: "And was his proposal so very sudden, then?"
MISS BRASSIE: "Sudden! Why, he didn't tee up at all. Simply plumped down on his knees and said, 'Let me caddie for you through the links of life'!"

VARIETY

MISS NIBLICK: "Don't you get tired of pl[ay]ing golf all the time?"
MISS BRASSIE: "Oh, yes. I often feel as i[f I] would like to stop playing and just sit down a[nd] talk about it."

By 1900 the ladies had invade[d] the golf links, as the two cartoo[ns] above, from 1900, show. On t[he] left, R. V. Cutler looks back [to] the nineties when croquet was t[he] most popular sport for mix[ed] company.

The styles of the day sometimes proved a factor in the popular game of croquet. For instance, the modish lady in the foreground, in strolling about awaiting her turn to play, has happened to drag her skirt across the ball leaving it — by the merest prank of fate — in a much better position for her next wicket.

OF COURSE
SPECTATOR: "What is the great attraction of the game?"
ONE OF THE PLAYERS: "Why, we are!"

Two *Puck* cartoons by Nankivell with but a single thought.

DO NOT EXCLUDE EACH OTHER
"Positively, I'd rather play polo than flirt."
"Fortunately, it is possible to do both at once."

UNWILLING TO TAKE CHANCES

"You must have confidence in yourself, Mama!"
"Well, I'll try, but — don't let go of me till I get it!"

Mamma had trouble with the bicycle, but Papa's real troubles came in with the automobile, as shown in the *Life* cartoon from 1906, below.

"I'm sorry, my dear, I can't find what's wrong. I'm afraid you'll have to walk."
"Why, George! I wouldn't ask the dog to walk on roads like these; you'll have to push the thing, that's all."

NO OBJECTION

"Can you swim?"
"Oh, yes! But I don't mind taking lessons!"

Rose O'Neill illustrates an eternal seashore theme, above, and F. Opper, below, records the rage for ping-pong in 1902.

Oh! Mother's been absent
for over a week;
We've had of her presence
Not even a peek.
Her Browning Home Circle
Is going it strong,
Pursuing a course in
Progessive Ping-pong!

Two views of baseball and football from *Puck* in 1909.

TO BE DEMONSTRATED

FAIR FAN: *"Tell me, Charlie, what's the squeeze play?"*
THE EXPERT: *"Oh, it would take too long to explain it here. I'll drop around this evening and show you!"*

PLAY BALL THERE! PLAY BALL!
WHEN YALE MEETS VASSAR ON THE AUTUMN GRIDIRON

*THE
TANNERY*

Some beach beauties, rolled stockings and all, drawn by *Life* Magazine's Popini in 1917.

GRANDMA: *"Now, don't loop me this morning, James. You know it makes me giddy."*

*"I had a strange sinking feeling when Tom
to kiss me."*
"Why? Hadn't you ever been kissed befor
"Never in an airplane."

Aviation was considered a new sport, and a new
thrill for young and old, in the twenties. Horse-
back riding also provided its kicks, as J. Norman Lynd shows on the right.

SOME HORSES WON'T PAY
ANY ATTENTION WHEN THEY'RE
TOLD TO "WHOA"...
SOMETIMES THE RIDING COSTUME
IS RESPONSIBLE

. . . your mother and I feel you should give up

"And in this corner, weighing none of your business . . ."

"THE AMAZONS"

"*Put your fingers in its eyes and your thumb in its mouth.*"

"*We're down here playing what-do-you-call-it!*"

"Who asked you to share my interests?"

There are some women, as George Price shows above, who use sports as an entry to a man's world, and others, such as Anatol Kovarsky's horsewoman, to whom a sport becomes an overriding mania.

IN A
MAN'S
WORLD

DOWN FROM THE VICTORIAN PEDESTAL TO THE "I'M-AS-GOOD-AS-ANY-MAN" WOMAN OF TODAY. SUFFRAGETTES AND STENOS, LADY EXECUTIVES AND DOCTORS, WACS, WAVES, AND WAR WORKERS. THE NEW WOMAN WITH HER KINDER, KUCHE, KIRCHE, UND CAREER.

*WOMAN'S
EMANCIPATION*

*(BEING A LETTER ADDRESSED TO MR. PUNCH,
WITH A DRAWING, BY A STRONG-MINDED AMERI-
CAN WOMAN)*

The first American Woman's Rights Convention took place at Seneca Falls, New York, in 1848, organized by Lucretia Mott and Elizabeth Cady Stanton. It was there that Amelia Jenks Bloomer showed up in her highly individual costume, adding a new word, "bloomers," to the language. In 1851 *Punch,* in England, ran a letter about the good fight, accompanied by the above drawing, and in 1852 *Harper's Weekly* ran the cartoon on the right depicting man as the weaker sex — a theme that was to become a favorite with the cartoonists.

*A GREAT
NUISANCE*

DASHING YOUNG LADY: "Will you allow me, Sir, the honor of escorting you home?"
MODEST YOUNG GENTLEMAN: "I thank you Miss. I will not trouble you. Mamma promised to send the carriage for me."

We see, above, another Woman's Rights Convention, as it appeared to a *Harper's Weekly* cartoonist in 1859. Below, a Currier & Ives dig at woman's rights, from 1869 The poster refers to "Susan Sharp-tongue" — undoubtedly Susan B. Anthony.

THE AGE OF BRASS

or the triumphs of Woman's Rights

THE ATLANTA SKATING CLUB.

THE SYREN FLIRTING CLUB.

THE PALLAS BILLIARD CLUB.

THE HIPPODAMIA DRIVING CLUB.

THE "GIRL OF THE PERIOD" — CLUB LIFE

Left, a cartoon by the great Thomas Nast, from 1872. Mr. Nast shows the colorful exponent of free love, Victoria Woodhull, being spurned by an overburdened woman who chooses the rocky path instead of Miss Woodhull's proffered primrose one. In the same era, below, other women were making paths for themselves as drummers and doctors. Good looks were no handicap, apparently.

"GET THEE BEHIND ME, (MRS.) SATAN!"
WIFE (with heavy burden): *"I'd rather travel the hardest path of matrimony than follow your footsteps."*

A SURE CURE

LADY PHYSICIAN: "H'm — he's very low. Who's your family physician?"
PATIENT'S WIFE: "Oh, family physician be hanged! Jes you hold on. He won't die so long's there's a young woman foolin' round him!"

THE FEMALE DRUMMER'S ART

A novel and successful method adopted as an experiment by two of the merchant princes of New York City.

WE ARE GETTING THERE FAST.

STERN PARENT: *"Willy, isn't that Miss Bloomers going soon? — it's nearly eleven o'clock."*
SON: *"Yes, Mama; she's just saying good night!"*

THE AMBASSADOR'S BALL IN DAYS TO COME

Charles Dana Gibson shows up in the 1890's with a pretty accurate bit of prognostication above, and another forecast, below, that has yet to come about.

A COUNCIL OF WAR IN DAYS TO COME

AN INAUGURATION OF THE FUTURE

Man's place is that of baby-tender in this cartoon by William H. Walker from 1897, as it was in the Currier & Ives print a few pages back.

CONVENTION OF THE HUSBAND REFORM CLUB
*SUBJECT FOR DISCUSSION AT THIS MEETING: — HOW TO MAKE THE HOME MORE
ATTRACTIVE*

*loomer-Girl-as-Battle-Axe in the Life car-
above. On the right Frank A. Nankivell
tes that the female stock-market dabblers
0 were not all Hetty Greens.*

HER FIRST EFFORT

MRS. BINTHARE: *"So you bought Westnorthern
for 98½?"*
MRS. JUSTINNIT: *"Yes; the broker's clerk told me
it had just been marked down from a hundred."*

THE BLOOMER GIRL'S WEDDING

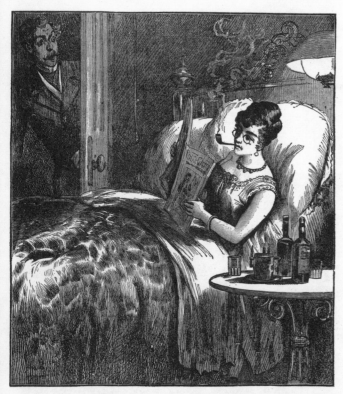

HOW SHE CURED HIM
A YOUNG WIFE ASTONISHES HER ERRATIC
HUSBAND BY EMULATING HIS EXAMPLE,
AND CAUSES HIM TO PROMPTLY ABAN-
DON THE VAGABOND HABITS OF HIS
BACHELOR DAYS.

MANAGER: "Unless you brace up I'll have
to break our contract."

"Don't say that! I have a child
and two husbands to support."

A picture (top) to put the fear of God into any man in 1896. *The Police Gazette* (above, left) in 1893 does a take-off on the errant husband, and (above, right) a view by Gibson of the problems of the distaff breadwinners.

THE LAST STRAW

FIRST OFFICE-BOY: "I'm going ter quit! Dat's de last straw!"
SECOND OFFICE-BOY: "What's de trouble?"
FIRST OFFICE-BOY: "Why, look at de new type-writer de boss has hired! A feller'd look nice takin' dat relic out ter lunch, wouldn't he?"

Women began taking office jobs in the 1880's, and within twenty years, when these cartoons appeared, had taken over all but a few of the secretarial chores.

"REPLYING TO YOURS OF RECENT DATE —"

If you are a busy man, the time you spend going to and from the office is dead waste. Take the hint.

94

WHY NOT GO THE LIMIT?

FOR THE BENEFIT OF THOSE LADIES WHO ASK THE RIGHT TO SMOKE IN PUBLIC

This richly detailed piece of humor by Henry Grant Dart from *Puck* in 1908 repays close scrutiny. Note the almonds and fudge on the free lunch.

THE ONLY WAY

SPEAKER: *"The only way we can gain woman's suffrage is by making our appeal through our charm, our grace, and our beauty."*

Three views of woman's suffrage, a big topic in the year 1912 (above) when John Held, Jr., made this acid comment, and in 1913 (below, right) and 1915 (below, left) in which the cartoonist, probably a male, has a woman poking fun at a suffragette.

SHE: *"You are too severe, James. Even the Suffragette is one of God's screechers."*

AN OUTRAGE

"There's still half an hour before the polls close, and they won't let me change my vote!"

THE ATTRACTION

BUSY BILL: *"Maybe I don't know politics, but I knows human nature in the cow country. That sign fetched 'em!"*

uffragettes *did* enjoy a certain popu-
in some parts of the country (above).
onist Orson Lowell (right), in 1913,
he possibility of the genteel woman
ng for political office, and at the same
takes a swipe at the Tammany Hall
politician.

HOSTESS: *"Miss Bleeker, let me introduce Mr. Terence Mulvaney. You candidates for office should know each other better."*

Two masters of nostalgia, Clare Briggs, above, and J. R. Williams, below, look at the harassing world of the schoolteacher.

"TAXI!"

WHEN WOMEN RUN THE BUSES

"A course of instruction has been opened for women so that they may take charge of buses in case of war." — News Item

The popular *Life* cartoonist J. Conacher (above) in a 1915 cartoon gives his view of the logical evolution of the masculine woman. In 1917 *Puck* (left) had fun with another prediction.

LIEUTENANT JANE: "The enemy are upon us!
What shall we do?"
COLONEL ISABEL: "M-m-b-l-m-b-m-l-m."

The cartoonists had a grand romp with the women in World War I. Life ran a series of cartoons by Popini (above) featuring the misadventures of a group of girls in uniform. Inwood's cartoon (below) could be used as a guide on what-not-to-do on a rifle range.

THE FIRST RIFLE PRACTISE OF THE WOMAN'S RESERVE CORPS

MESSENGER: "The Major wants to know if you will please excuse him from reviewing the practise today. He doesn't feel strong enough."

Pigs is pigs—but

Milkin' Time

The Hired Woman

The Old Swimming Hole

Saturday Night

With the able-bodied men all overseas, the able-bodied women took over their jobs on the farm (left), as shown by Rea Irvin, and in the factories (below, left).

DOWN ON THE FARM WITH THE WOMAN WAR WORKERS

THE GIRL HE LEFT BEHIND HIM: "Don't you remember your little Annie?"

AT WQMAN'S TRAINING CAMP YOUNG OFFICER (somewhat flustered): "Squabs — er Squads — Right!"

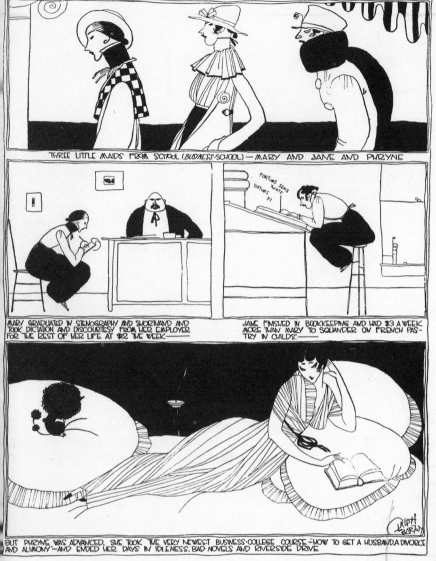

"THREE LITTLE MAIDS FROM SCHOOL —"

The great caricaturist Ralph Barton (above) does a take-off on the booming post-war business schools for women. H. T. Webster (right) indicates that many of the women war-workers found it profitable to stay on at the factory after the war's end.

"Fifteen dollars a week fer teachin' school? I a darn shame! They oughta give ya eighteen twenty dollars. Why, I'm gettin' forty dolle down to th' factory!"

Nineteenth Amendment, giving the
 to women, was passed by Congress
920. Oliver Herford's cartoon (right)
eared in *Life* on December 30, 1920.
. Peters (below) in one of a spate of
oons kidding the woman voter.

"It's a girl!"

"And whom did you vote for, Miss Sophy?"
*"Well, you see, the Republican was simply stunningly good-
looking. But the Democrat had always been perfectly splendid
to his family, so I marked both ballots, closed my eyes, shuffled
them, put one in the box and tore up the other. Nothing could
be fairer than that."*

EQUAL RIGHTS FOR MEN

Two amusing views of equal rights, both from 1921. That was the year women began to bob their hair and invade the barber shops.

THE CANDIDATES GO AFTER THE FEMININE

105

AN IMPRESSION OF A WOMAN'S COLLEGE

By One Who Has Never Been There

A masculine view of woman's education, by Ellison Hoover. One of a series of "An Impression of . . . " that ran in *Life* in 1925.

Some women were getting along in the business world, and some were not. Lucy Stone was a strong-minded feminist who married one Henry Blackwell in 1855, but refused to give up her maiden name. The Lucy Stone League enjoyed a revival in the 1920's. Art Young's cartoon, below, appeared in *The Masses*.

FIRST LUCY STONER: "But, my dear, you were always so keen on George! Why turn him down?"
SECOND LUCY STONER: "Don't be silly, Helen; you know perfectly well his last name is the same as mine."

Women who did succeed in business were given a hard time by cartoonist Gardner Rea.

THE HIGH SALARIED LADY EXECU-
TIVE REVERTS TO TYPE

IMPRESSIONS OF MAGAZINE OFFICES
Vogue

Came the depression, and the workin[g]
found herself walking the tightrope of [work]
and home, as illustrated in the two carto[ons by]
I. Klein (left). In New York City caree[r women]
would double up in furnished rooms, a[nd try]
to outwit the "no cooking" rule.

"But precious, why didn't you think of that
before?"

"Oh, George, I'm working overtime. When you
get home will you start the potatoes?"

"Quick, Ella, hide the stove, the landlady['s]
coming."

"Hello, Momma, we're makin' history."

...mous cartoons of the thirties, by Denys ...an (above), and Robert Day (right).

"For Gosh sakes, here comes Mrs. Roosevelt!"

The Thrill that Comes Once in a Lifetime. By Webster

Although in uniform, women were women still in World War II.

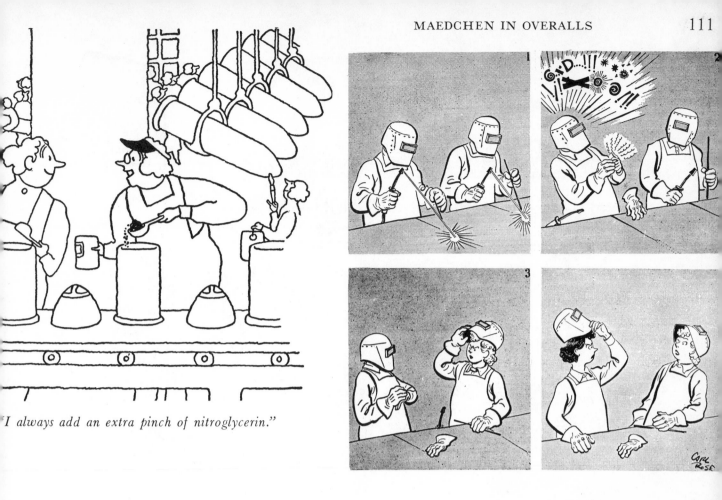

"I always add an extra pinch of nitroglycerin."

The women war workers as seen by Gardner Rea, Carl Rose, and Francis W. Dahl.

IT HAPPENED ON THE EL

"You gah dam pussy cats!"

© 1934 The New Yorker Magazine, Inc.

"Why Not Go the Limit?" was the title of Harry Grant Dart's forward-looking cartoon of 1908. The limit was approached about thirty years later, and commented on with some acidity by James Thurber and Cobean.

"I can lick any woman in the house!"

© 1947 The New Yorker Magazine, Inc.

"I must show you the room I had when I was in college."

"Thank goodness I finally have something to report at our Vassar reunion!"

Some contemporary cartoons on the
inine sex as doctor, nurse, and baby-si

Frank Owen

"*What's the matter — lost your nerve?*"

AL KAUFMAN

"*I don't care if they have
television — you get right b
to where you're supposed to
babysitting!*"

. *11:30* A.M. *2:30* P.M. *4:15* P.M. *5:30* P.M.

*Chon Day (left) on an office tradition, an[d]
comments by the perceptive W. E. Hill o[n]
girls."*

chon
Day

*"Why don't you chase me around the office like
other executives do?"*

*These gals, all from an
auditing department, are
throwing a going-away
luncheon in honor of a co-
worker who is leaving to
get married. (It's at one of
those little Italian pizza
places, this one known as
Antonio's Cavern, all de-
corated with imitation
stalactites.) Later they'll
present the bride-to-be
with a beautiful percolator.*

*Another secretary. She brings her
lunch — salmon sandwiches and a
banana for dessert, prepared by her
lovely ma. Eats it at her boss's desk,
and he will smell salmon, mayon-
naise, and banana all afternoon.*

"You're beautiful, you're lovely, you're adorable. You should go places. Say the word and I'll put you on the County Committee."

"I wouldn't go overboard dear — everybody gets jury duty from time to time."

"I'm giving my new Congressman six months to do something, and after that — watch out!"

THE TV COMMERCIAL GIRLS

Here are W. E. Hill's ideas on the career girl of the fifties — she's in advertising, acting, and modeling all at the same time.

Weather girl. Intensely [...]able, and after telling you [...] the masses of cold air re[...] come down from Canada [...] look you square in the e[...] tell how, unlike the we[...] which is often unpredi[...] you can always depend [...] sponsor's margarine. "Do[...] ask for margarine at your [...] ite chain store, ask for 'Wo[...] the all-purpose margarine[...]

Instant coffee girl. She's all agog over the new instant coffee that isn't a powder, but is all tiny coffee beans, with that almost unbelievable locked-in coffee taste and so nut-flavorish.

Dishwashing girl. She uses "Shove" in her dishwasher now, and what used to be a chore is just one great big lark. It makes dishwashing such fun!

Interview with commercials thrown in. She's interviewing an author about his new book, "Two years With Head Hunters," and interrupts him every other sentence to tell her audience about "Gluey," the happy cake ingredient, the rich, fluffy shortening. Or about "Delight," the hair shampoo. So light, so fluffy.

Deodorant girl. Always expensive-looking and somewhat pensive as she sprays something called "petite" on her. This deodorant is guaranteed not to trickle, won't tickle, and will keep one odorless for a week.

MANNERS, MORALS, AND THE SOCIAL WHIRL

THE REVOLT AGAINST THE PURITAN TRADITION. FROM BLUSHES TO BLASPHEMY. THE BRIDGE GAME, THE DANCE, AND THE WOMAN'S CLUB. FLAMING YOUTH, FREE LOVE, AND DIVORCE.

ART AND NATURE

"Mama, dear, when shall we come to any more of those pictures where I have to put my fan up?"

HER POINT OF VIEW

SHOCKED PARENT: "Lily, my dear! D *you consider cigarette smoking a proper hab* *for a decorous young lady?"* *DAUGHTER OF EMANCIPATED IDEAS* *"No, papa dear; if I thought it was, I'd —* *shoot it."*

(Papa is much relieved.)

No nice girl in the 1880's looked at nude pictures, smoked or read those shocking French novels. *Puck* magazine, however, suspected that a *few* did.

THE INCREASING POPULARITY OF THE FRENCH NOVEL

THE LADIES WANT IT, BUT THEY ARE ASHAMED
TO ASK FOR IT.

HER OFFENSE

*ASKINS: "Don't you belong to a reading club, Miss
Somers?"*
*MISS SOMERS: "Yes; but I'm afraid they'll expel
me. I've been found guilty of talking about a dozen
books I haven't read!"*

The idea of young ladies having any lit-
erary interest was ridiculed by cartoonists
at the turn of the century.

WISER THAN WE SEEM

*MISS W. (from Boston): "Why, Ella, how
delightful! Here's a complete set of Molière."*
ELLA: "Molly Eyre?"
*MISS W.: "Yes, I never supposed you cared
for that sort of reading."*
ELLA: "Indeed I do, I just dote on her!"

ONE FOR BOSTON

NEW YORKER (who has been "stuck" more than an hour with an intellectual young lady from Boston): "You say you despise New York men. Then why do you come to New York, and why do you go to New York parties?"

YOUNG LADY FROM BOSTON: "For a complete intellectual rest."

The Boston women were considered intellectual snobs — blueblooded bluestockings (above). With the *nouveaux riche,* the surest way to social success was through having English relations, either living or dead (below).

A GENIUS

MRS. NEWLYRICH: "Everything you have you owe to me!"

MR. NEWLYRICH (groaning): "Yes! Even them slob ancestors are your idea!"

INTERNATIONAL

LORD HEAVYDEBTS: "I have got to do something, by jove! And your tin is needful, you know. I hate your beastly loud voice and manners, but, er — let's marry, you know."

MISS DOUBLEDOLLAR: "I like somebody else better, but just think of the style I could put on — well, I am your girl!"

The flowing style of Otho Cushing makes a prediction about morals and dress in 1899 (left). Another aspect of the social life of the period were the parlor sopranos, who felt themselves called upon to entertain at all upper-class soirées.

GLIMPSES INTO THE FUTURE
The stage in the near future, as promised by present indications.

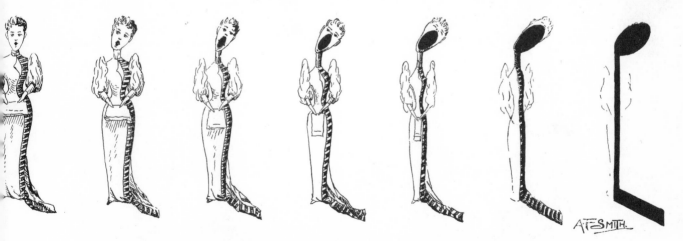

HOW AN ARDENT MUSICAL ASPIRANT, REACHING FOR
HIGH C, BECAME A WOMAN OF NOTE.

THE OLD FASHIONED GIRL WHO TURNED THE PICTURES FACE TO THE WALL BEFORE UNDRESSING.
—GAAR WILLIAMS + S.B.

BORN THIRTY YEARS TOO SOON

J.R.WILLIAMS 12-13
T. M. Reg. U. S. Pat. Off.
Copr. 1954 by NEA Service, Inc.

Modesty marked the lady of the nineties. Here are backward glances to that time by Gaar Williams (above, left) and J. R. Williams (above, right), and a contemporary cartoon from *Life* by Penrhyn Stanlaws.

P. STANLAWS

"Yes, madame; certainly. Anything else? We have a nice line of men's —....

........underwear."

The doorway with the homey title, up every side street in the "live-and-let-live" nineties, where the fair sex could offset a hard day's washing by "rushing the growler." ("A pint of dark, Gus, and not too much collar this time!") This inconspicuous portal of cheer was also a boon to husbands of W.C.T.U.'S and overrash individuals who — in an unguarded moment — had sworn off.

One of R. V. Cutler's series "The Gay Nineties," which ran in *Life* during the nineteen twenties (above). J. R. Williams looks back at two other sacred institutions of the nineties: respect for parents (below, left) and the afternoon social visit (below, right).

THE HORSEHAIR SOFA

The horseless buggy, which came in
the new century, was seen by Samue[l]
Ehrhart (left) as an aid to romance,
by Gordon Grant (below) as a mon[ster]
which transformed nice people into de[mons]
Time has proved both to be correct.

ADVICE

*HE: "We are thirty-two miles from home and
this automobile is a wreck. There's only one
thing to be done."*
SHE: "And that?"
*HE: "Why, seek shelter in the nearest parson-
age!"*

HER FIRST RIDE   *A MONTH LATER*

DEVILUTION

A WEDDING A LA TANGO

SOME PEOPLE PREFER THE OLD STEPS

e Tango was introduced to America in
10, and swept the country, starting a
ncing rage that horrified the puritans.
e wedding cartoon (above), from *Judge*
1913 is one of the earliest appearances
John Held, Jr.

AT HOME WITH THE BLUES

THE SOLACE OF PSYCHOANALYSIS

The only Polite and Painless Cure for Human Faults and Failin

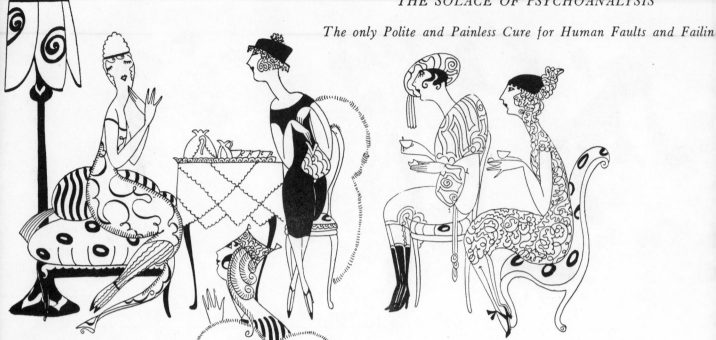

SOLOPHOBIA — AND THE ONLY CURE FOR IT

Alicia Wilberforce suffered terribly from one of the most painful forms of mental distress, the dreadful Fear of Being Alone! Without someone — preferably a man — to talk to — she almost died. Now she is telling her friends, Miriam, Elspeth, Hildegarde, and Cynthia, how she finally met wonderful Dr. Knuck, the psychoanalyst. "He is a dear, my dears!" she says — "and he understands me so perfectly. 'You are lonely' he said, holding my hand before I left him — 'what you need most is companionship and affection —' And then he looked into my eyes —" but Alicia can get no further — "His address" cry all the ladies, "Give us his address!"

There was a general loosening up of morals after World War I. Fish, who was to become a star contributor, gives us an early intimation of the spread of psychoanalysis in a 1921 issue of *Vanity Fair* (above). The cartoon by John Held, Jr. (right), from *Life* in 1923, is one of the most representative comments on the flapper era.

"The trouble with you boys today is you have no imagination!"
"Well, girlie, nowadays we don't need imagination."

If men should entertain their friends as wom do.

THE DANCE-MAD YOUNGER SET

more typical John Held, Jr., cartoons
e twenties. The Charleston (right)
t the country in 1926, and enjoyed a
al thirty years later when it was a
re of the Broadway success. *The Boy*
d.

Teaching Old Dogs New Tricks

"Mother, when you were a girl, didn't you find it a bore to be a virgin?"

The collapse of morals in the late twenties is pointed up in a classic cartoon by Art Young (above) and in an early cartoon of Peter Arno's, from *Life*.

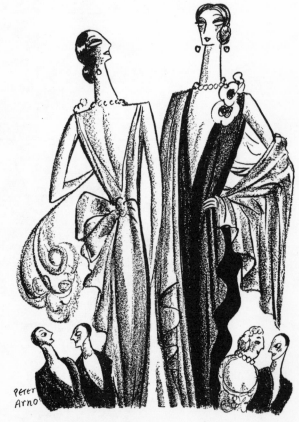

"And your first husband? How was he?"
"Oh — he was the nicest one of all. Beginner's luck, you know."

The Evening MODERNE — Mixing and blending the bathtub gin

Mother makes the faux pas of asking her young daughter what time her friends will bring her home.

Prohibition provided early do-it-yourself pursuits for young Americans (above). Crawford Young (left) in a 1927 *Ladies' Home Journal* cartoon, shows us that parental authority had become a laughing matter.

"I certainly have NOT *got a match! And what's more, if I had I wouldn't give it to you."*

Even as late as 1928 some die-hard old-sters spoke out against women smoking in public (above). Divorce had created confusion in young minds (left), as shown in this *Life* cartoon in 1930. Later in the thir-ties *Ballyhoo* Magazine enjoyed a flurry of success. Here (below right) is one of their more sedate comments on the morals of the time.

"And take care of mother and father, mother's husband and father's wife and mother's fiancé!"

"Mother doesn't mind so long as I don't play for money."

"Avez-vous 'Ulysses'?"

Two views of Helen Hokinson's famous
clubwomen, showing their interest in two
very different varieties of literature.

*"I don't believe it's generally known that Mrs. Birt-
well has had a poem accepted by 'Driftwind.'"*

© 1947 The New Yorker Magazine, Inc.

"*They're terribly strict in here about soliciting. You can set your can on the table, but they won't let you shake it.*"

The American woman of the Helen Hokinson class devoted much of her time to good works.

"I don't care if this is a tango, George Taylor. When the music stops I'm going to slap your face!"

WHY MOTHERS GET GRAY

HIONS IN MANNERS

BRIDGE

"I'm beautiful, intelligent, wealthy and happy.
What's wrong with me?"

HUSBAND, HOME, AND CHILD

SHOWING WOMAN WHERE THE HEART IS (OR WAS). FROM
HONEYMOON TO HOUSEWORK, FROM RUNNING MAIDS TO
RUNNING GADGETS. THE SCENE OF THE MAJOR ENGAGEMENTS
OF THE BATTLE BETWEEN THE SEXES.

WOMEN'S RIGHTS

*YOUNG LADY: "Father, have you ever heard a
lecture on Women's Rights?"*
*PARENT: "Well, yes, I may say I have; and it has
lasted for twenty years."*

As far back as the 1860's the American woman had a firm grip on her husband, and
was sure to let him know her place (above). F. Opper (below) was the most popular
cartoonist in America from the 1880's through to the first World War. He worked
particularly for *Puck* and for Hearst papers.

MAKE NO MISTAKE!

*CAREFUL WIFE: "Now, Henry, don't forget. The band around your hat means that you must order that
medicine at the druggist's; the string around your finger is for the theatre tickets; the bow on your arm is
to remind you to post my letter to my mother, and the knot in your handkerchief is for that paper of needles.
Good-by, dear, and be careful of yourself."*

Two unsentimental comments on honey-mooners, from *Puck* in 1889 (left), and Harper's Bazar in 1868 (below).

HE KNEW HIS LESSON
MRS. HUNNIMUNE *(reproachfully)*: "Why, surely, John, you're not going into the smoking car?"
MR. HUNNIMUNE: "Of course I am. Didn't you say we must act in public like old married people?"

THE HONEYMOON

FULL MOON

FIRST QUARTER

THIRD QUARTER

NO MOON

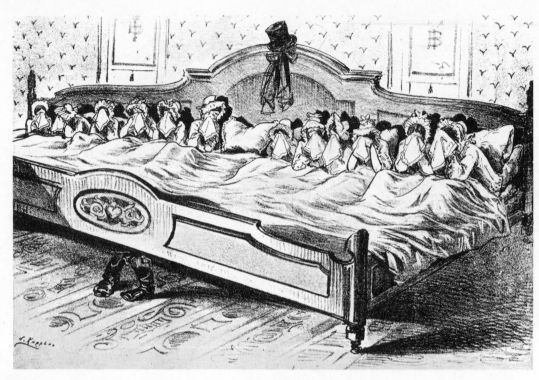

IN MEMORIAM BRIGHAM YOUNG
"AND THE PLACE WHICH KNEW HIM ONCE SHALL KNOW HIM NO MORE."

When Brigham Young, Mormon leader and polygamist, died in 1877, leaving a quantity of widows, Joseph Keppler of *Puck* limned this heartrending scene (above). F. Opper (below) told the story of a widow whose period of mourning had apparently passed. From *Puck,* 1880.

THEY MET BY CHANCE—A TALE OF THE CENSUS

The Meeting

"Your name, please?"

"Are you a native of this country?"

"You are a widow, I believe?"

Fourth question (not in the list):
"Do you wish to remain a widow any longer?"

Fifth question: "Your age, please"

THE FRENCH FLAT OF THE VERY NEAR FUTURE
EVERYTHING ON THE PREMISES

IN THE KITCHEN

IN THE PARLOR

The first New York City luxury apartment houses were known as "French flats." F. Opper's conception of what they were to become, drawn for *Puck* in 1883, contained intimations of the radio, the supermarket, and facsimile newspapers.

THE WANING OF THE HONEYMOON — Scene, Richfield Springs

WIFE (to husband who has promised to spend the evening at home): "Do take some coffee."
HUSBAND: "No, it keeps me awake."

Two cynical views of marriage from *Life* in 1885.

SHE DOTES UPON HIS VERY ABSENCE

RECTOR'S WIFE (to young Mrs. Montague Brown): "What! Your husband has gone to town and left you again for another week! A nice way to treat you! I thought you said he was so charming."
MRS. M. B.: "So I did, and is not that his greatest charm?"

Two cartoons by F. Opper poking fun at middle-class marriage in the 1880's.

YOUNG HUSBAND: "Now, love, which will you have — the chatelaine watch, the bracelets, or the necklace?"
YOUNG WIFE: "We must avoid unnecessary expense, dear. I'm sure if you buy all three the man will give you a reduction on them. I'm your own saving, economical little wifey, ain't I?"

THE AGE OF HANDBOOKS

"I think you are perfectly horrid, to find fault with the dinner, Henry; I got it all out of the 'Young Housekeeper's Infallible Cook-Book,' and it ought to be good, I'm sure."

Life with Father and Mother was gay in the nineties, especially when Father played tricks like this one (left). Mama had problems with the servants (below, left), and the servants had problems with Mama (below, right), especially when she got the decorating bug.

MRS. KILLINGLEIGH: *"Great heaven! The man's misfortunes have turned his head!"*
MR. KILLINGLEIGH: *"Don't worry, my dear. I've got to attend a creditor's meeting today, and I want this to show that I've something valuable left to resume business on!"*

THE REASON

"Why did your nurse leave?"
"The baby came down with the mumps, and it seems the policeman had never had them."

USEFUL AS WELL AS ORNAMENTAL

NEW GIRL: *"Please, Mum, I can't make pie crust without a rollin' pin."*
MRS. DE KORATER: *"You'll find it hanging in the parlor. Remove the ribbons and hooks, and scrape off the gold paint before you use it."*

ON THE WEDDING JOURNEY

THIS IS ABOUT HOW IT SEEMS TO THOSE OBJECTS OF INTEREST, THE BRIDE

AND GROOM

On the honeymoon journey, as Charles Dana Gibson saw it, the couple endured mutual agony. But later the wife could part quite coolly from her husband, with her mind on more practical things.

HIS WIFE: "Good-by, dear. Write often, if it's only a check."

WARNING TO NOBLEMEN
TREAT YOUR AMERICAN WIFE WITH KINDNESS

Charles Dana Gibson and Samuel D. Ehrhart warn foreign noblemen that the American girls can take care of themselves.

QUITE A DIFFERENCE

LORD TUFFNUTT: *"You have nothing to grumble at; you were a rich American girl, I am an impoverished English nobleman with a proud title. You bought me with your wealth. I was what you call, in shopping, a bargain!"*

LADY TUFFNUTT: *"Pardon me! Not a bargain— a remnant."*

"How peaceful it looks in there."

A PAINFUL DIFFERENCE

WHEN MOTHER IS HURT   WHEN FATHER IS HURT

INFLATED

NURSE (to ditto): "Fat? Sure, it ain't fat, it's wind; yer see, the poor dear was brought up on one o' them pnoomatic breast-forms."

Two digs at the neglectful mother, by L Glackens, a *Puck* regular for twenty (above), and O'Neill Latham (left).

MADAM'S IDEA

HUSBAND: "So you attended Madam Sayloot' lecture on 'How to Bring up Children.' How did she handle the subject?"
WIFE: "Oh, wretchedly! She stood up there and advised mothers to stay home and take care of their children instead of running around listening to lectures about it!"

Two ever popular jokes about marriage, done in high style at the turn of the century by Arthur E. Jameson (left) and Charles Dana Gibson (below).

WIFE: *"I thought you told me you were well off before you married me."*

HUSBAND: *"I am sure of it now, my dear!"*

A CONTINUOUS PERFORMANCE
SHE: *"It tells here of a man in Chicago who hasn't spoken to his wife in fifteen years."*
HE: *"Perhaps he is waiting for a chance."*

"MY WIFE'S HOME FROM THE COUNTRY, HOO-RAY, HOO-RAY!"

Two sides of marriage by Gordon Grant, from *Puck* in 1909.

POST-NUPTIAL GLIMPSES

THE MAN WHO MARRIED THAT CLEVER LITTLE EMOTIONAL ACTRESS

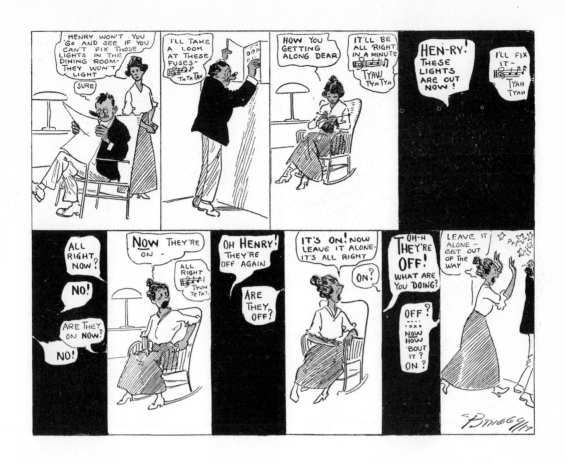

Two from Clare Briggs's delightful and discerning series "A Handy Man Around the House."

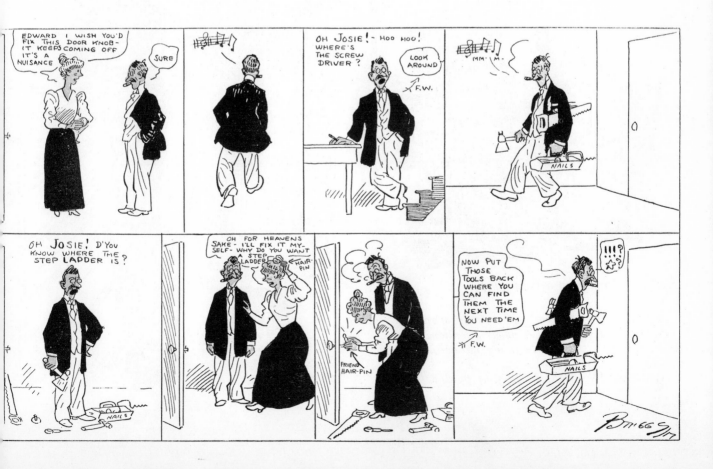

"JUST A WORD OF ADVICE— YOU HAVE TO SHOW 'EM FROM THE START THAT YOU'RE THE BOSS!"

The American mother-in-law has always been powerful force in marriage, but the husban could sometimes get back at her.

THAT'S DIFFERENT

WYDEMAN: "Excuse me, young man, but I think your mother needs attention."
NAHROW: "The lady is my mother-in-law."
WYDEMAN: "Oh! I beg your pardon."

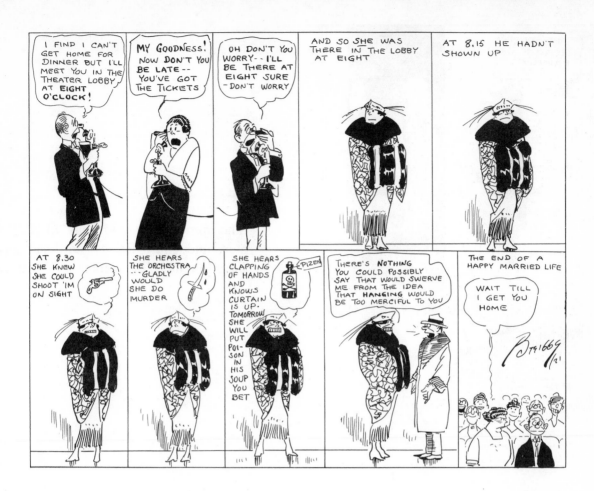

WHAT THEY CALL THEIR WIVES

The immortal "Timid Soul" of H. T. Webster, and Clare Briggs' harassed husband have long been brothers in misfortune.

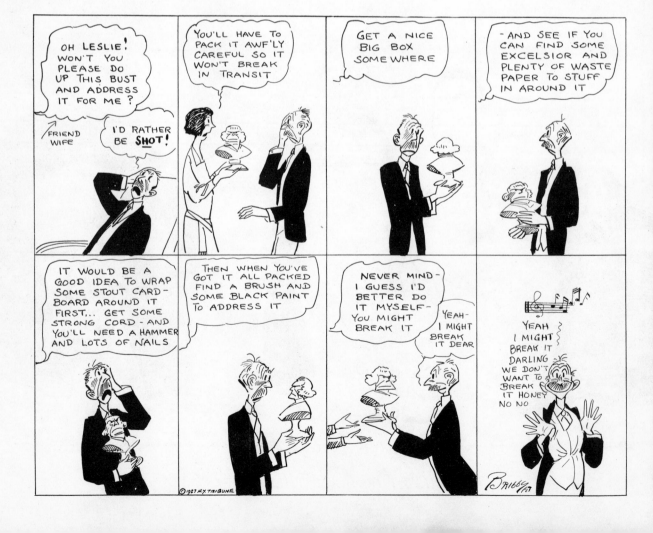

IT'S RATHER TOUGH ON MOTHER

After years and years of this

and this

and this

and this

and this — *always to be remembered*

more or less like this!

"Don't cry — be little and I'll be your mother."

Two views of mother-and-child from Denys Wortman's *Metropolitan Movies*.

*"Wilbur, stop that, and chew your gum refined like
mama does."*

"By gorry, I'm tired."

*"There you go! You're tired! Here I be a'standin' over a hot stove all day, an'
you're workin' in a nice cool sewer!"*

*"Come, Sadie, get your mind off sinks and garbage
pails."*

One of the three or four most famous cartoons in history (above) by the Masses
artist, Art Young, and a typical Sidney
Hoff situation (left).

"It's broccoli, dear."

"I say it's spinach, and I say the hell with it."

Carl Rose's classic cartoon on one of the defects of the progressive method of child-rearing (above), and a comment by Gardner Rea (below) on an old-fashioned, non-progressive way of husband-rearing.

"Don't bother Daddy, darling. He's had a hard day at the office."

"You've got to take it easier, Mrs. Beedle. Stop driving your husband so hard."

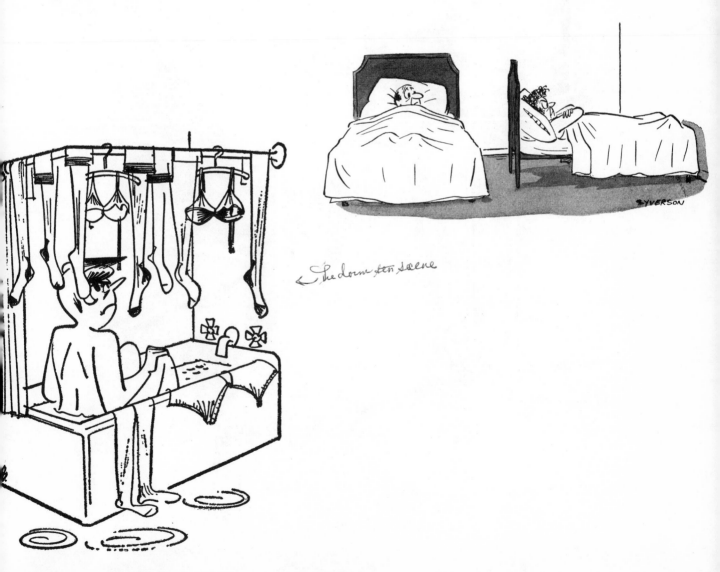

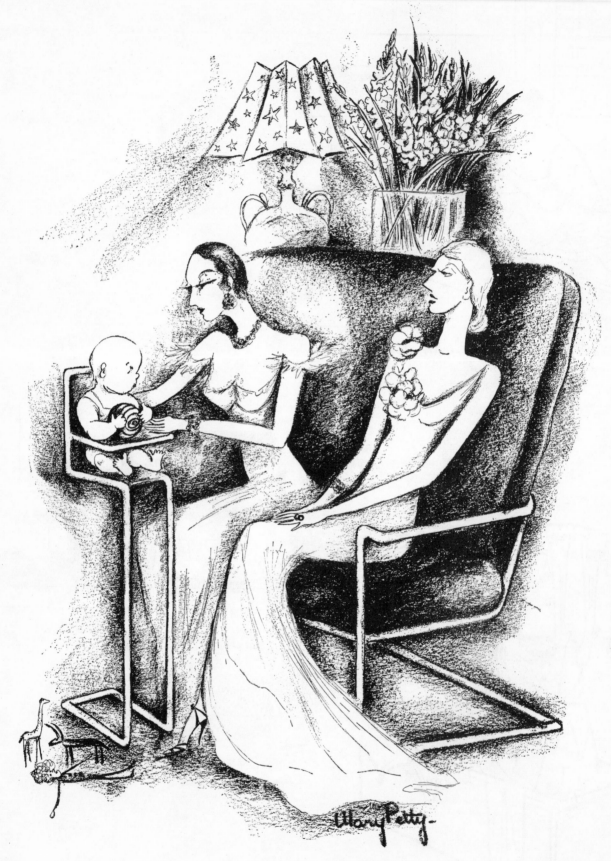

"I wouldn't kiss him, dear — it might cause a maladjustment later on."

"You only think of one thing!"

William Steig's comment (above), which appeared in 1932, was authenticated in 1948 upon the publication of Professor Alfred Kinsey's *Sexual Behavior in the Human Male* (below).

"Wonderful cookbook, dear! Once I started reading,
I just couldn't put it down."

"Do you think for one split second that I like
my cooking any better than you do?"

Some comments on the pains and pleasures of motherhood by Virgil Partch (left), Ted Key (below, left), and Bernhardt (below, right).

, suppose we let Ellie do it her own way."

"Now children, behave. Children! Boys!"

James Thurber's famous psychologic[a]
toon about marriage (left), and a
pleasant view by Alan Dunn (below)

*"Oh, I meant to tell you — it wasn't psychoso-
matic after all."*

Mary Petty (left) shows us the hazardous life of a domestic in a "Back to Nature Modern" house. An illustration from T. H. Robsjohn-Gibbings' book *Homes of the Brave*. Maids pretty much went out with World War II, but Ted Key's popular "Hazel" (below) stayed on — perhaps because the cartoonist couldn't afford to let her go.

"How about . . ."

"It's about time you learned to dress yourself!"

"This is his muse speaking."

"Ruthie? My mother says over her dead body too."

Two conflicting views of woman's burde
by Chon Day (left) and Cobean (below

"Occupation?"

"Woman."

And finally, to offset much that we have seen before about the battle of the sexes, a reminder from B. Tobey that warmth and affection *do* exist in the American home.

THE ETERNAL WOMAN

SOME OF THE FACTS AND FALLACIES ABOUT WOMAN ANYWHERE,
ANY TIME. GOSSIP, ILLOGIC, CURIOSITY, AND THE DESIRE FOR
CHANGE. HYPOCHONDRIA AND EXTRAVAGANCE, THE CLICHES OF
THE FRIENDLY ICEMAN AND THE PAMPERED LAP DOG.

CAMPAIGN DUTY

"My dear, what are you doing?"
"Practicing, my love, practicing for our little exodu

Three aspects of the eternal feminine as seen by cartoonists of the 1870's: regarding the husband as a beast of burden (above), a desire to impress the neighbors (below, left), and a tendency to exaggeration (below, right).

BOUND TO BE SHOWN

MISS DORA: *"Jane, take all these under-clothes, wet them, and hang them out to dry."*
JANE: *"Why, miss, they've not been worn yet!"*
MISS DORA: *"No matter. There's a new family moved opposite, and I want them to see what nice things I've got."*

LADY: *"For pity's sake, how often do th cars run? I've been waiting here a week."*
SATIRICAL CONDUCTOR: *"Have y ma'am? That's strange — I was by here th days ago, and never noticed you!"*

THE MOMENTOUS QUESTION OF SPRING BONNETS

BROWN'S WIFE: "One more word, dear. Would you trim it with blue feathers?"
ROBINSON'S WIFE: "Oh, I couldn't decide at once. Come to me tomorrow,
and we'll devote the whole day to it."

An 1878 view of woman's favorite topic for intense discussion: clothes (above), and,
from 1883 (below) the eternal window shopper.

A NEGLECTED CLASS

"Isn't it about time the storekeepers made some provision for the comfort of
window shoppers"?

WHISPERED

THE FRIEND: "Her face is her fortune."
*THE ENEMY: "How interesting! Made it he[r]
too, didn't she?"*

Charles Dana Gibson on cattiness (above) and Samuel D. Ehrhart, (below) on the strong-minded wife.

DISCOURAGING

CLARA: "He is so obstinate."
MAUDE: "In what way?"
*CLARA: "It's the hardest thing in the world to
convince him that I am always right."*

THEY ARE ONLY COLLECTING THE USUAL FANS AND GLOVES

Gibson on woman's eternal propensity for misplacing small articles, and Frank A. Nankivell on the bargaining value of tears.

WHAT MADE HIM SURRENDER

MRS. QUIZZER: "Did that lovely gown cost you much?"
MRS. KNOWALL: "Only one good cry!"

Ehrhart on woman's unreasonableness, and F. M. Howarth showing the older woman's weakness for lap dogs.

I.

II.

III.   IV.

V.

AN INQUIRY

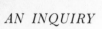

MR. NEWLYWED: *"I'm willing to do anything you wish if it's reasonable."*
MRS. NEWLYWED: *"Oh! Why waste time considering whether it's reasonable?"*

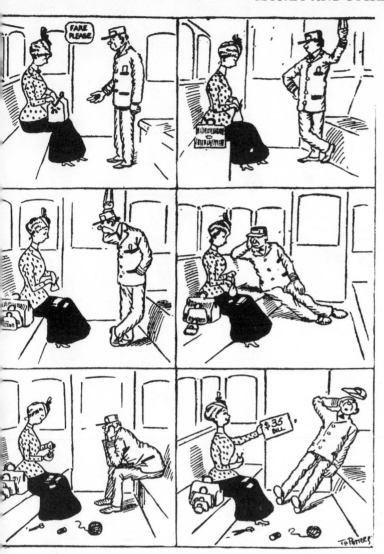

REFUTED

HE: "Everybody knows that women are more talkative than men."
SHE: "Never. Mr. Taft accepted the nomination in fifteen thousand words, and I'd like to see a woman who couldn't snap up a proposal in less time than that."

T. E. Powers, the immensely popular Hearst cartoonist (left) on a problem that has been with us since barter went out, and Nankivell (above) on woman's strong sense of realism when dealing with vital situations. The immigrant women of New York's lower East Side in 1902 (below) are shown by Rose O'Neill enjoying a pleasant gossip about the neighbors.

NO RESCUE

MAG: "She's goin' ter marry de feller dat jumped off de Brooklyn Bridge."
LIZ: "Well, he won't find no tugboat waitin' ter pick him up after dis jump!"

TWO MILES FROM HOME

*ROSALIND: "Now dear, wait here a minute
while I go into Madam Dupe's and select a hat."
HUBERT: "A minute, eh? Well, it's very cold,
I've got to keep my engine running, you know,
and there's only ten gallons of gasoline."*

L·FELLOWS·

A beautiful period drawing from *Judge* in
1915 (above) which points out that there
are imperfections in woman's sense of time,
and (right) a comment from the same year
on the delights of a good cry.

THOROUGHLY ENJOYING THE PLAY

THE SEVEN DEADLY TEMPERAMENTS

As Frequently Met With in the Ladies — God Bless 'Em

aspects of the female character as seen by Fish of *Vanity Fair* in 1917.

THE FELINE TEMPERAMENT

Four members of the feline, velvet-pawed, low-springing, meat-eating cat family, shown in the act of trepanning little Angela, the sweet, blond, yielding, and wholly worshipful being who is seated on the Davenport sofa before you. There is not one single nasty thing that the felines have forgotten to say about Angela, a girl who has never done a wrong thing in all her life — except that she allowed Destiny to make her irresistibly attractive to married men.

THE MATERNAL TEMPERAMENT

THE SOULFUL TEMPERAMENT

Always devoted to calla lillies, rhythmic (or self-expression) dancing, and loose-fitting Greek robes. She usually displays an abnormal interest in what's what on the buffet. Leave this type of girl alone with a tableful of truffles, pâtés, mushrooms, macaroons, queen olives, peaches, and chocolate éclairs, and the place, after a brief interval, will take on the appearance of Bapaume, after its evacuation by the Germans.

Here we see the ideal mother, the Chatelaine type, a type upon which so many poets, novelists, and music-hall singers have dilated at length — in two-part time. The future of the race is hers. It is a trifle hard to tell — when you see her separated from her little ones — whether she is an Elsie de Wolfe sofa pillow or a marble parquet floor. This type of lady is always irresistible to the clergy, especially when they are of the Protestant Episcopal persuasion. As will be observed, upon a somewhat closer scrutiny of her and her biological factor, the union has been fairly fruitful.

You know the kind. She simply won
alone. Picking on you, all day lo
starts right in on you at breakfas
with the coffee and the toast. Sh
gets up early and comes down all
and ready for a good day's naggin,
is no known form of temperamen
rible, so poisonous, so soul-blightin,
so certain to marry. No wonder
demure little daughter has decided
to musical comedy and never, neve
to enter the married state. Oh, ye
and mothers, what a wonderful le
truthful picture should be to you

THE ARTISTIC TEMPERAMENT

Last, but most frequently met with of all,
we behold the artistic temperament. By
that we mean the lady who feels things so
keenly, suffers so acutely, and kicks so
ferociously, that we know instinctively, on
observing her, that she is passionately devoted to ART. Have you noticed that they
always wear clinging Annette Kellerman
garments, and that they are very rude to
the maid?

THE ROMANTIC TEMPERA

Cupid just leads her around from c
corner to another and from on
soldier to another brave soldier. S
exclusively upon little penciled
Chocolate bon-bons, pressed violet
Shelley, moonlight, mandolins, a
strains of "The Rosary." Very da
to a man in his first season. Equa
gerous to a man in the bald-heade
but particularly dangerous to a ma
— not to say doddering — with ag

THE PRACTICAL TEMPERAMENT

A frequent and highly commendable type
of womanhood. She always knows exactly
what she wants — which is usually something under the classification of Jewelry.
Furthermore, she knows how to get it, and
she knows where to go for it. In short, she
is a ferret, a sharp-shooter, a good egg.
(All of these are vulgar slang terms for
pippins, baby-stares, Jumbo squabs, ante-
lopes, and chicken pot-pies.) Note: The
serious part of the creature's work is
achieved solely by the power of the eye.

THE MORTAL AGONY OF THE AVERAGE MAN IN A TEA-ROOM

Jones doesn't really look like this — it's the way he feels.

Showing (above) that there are places in a woman's world where men should *never* go, and (below) a take-off on the matinee idol.

WILL IT COME TO THIS?

IT HAPPENS IN THE BEST REGULATED FAMILIES

Clare Briggs conducted the earliest, and the best, of the husband-and-wife newspaper strips.

*FATHER'S MENTAL PICTURE OF WHAT MOTHER AND
THE GIRLS ARE DOING AT NEWPORT*

The luxurious style of the *Life* cartoonist, Popini, commenting in 1920 on the popular belief that women just spend and spend.

DIPLOMACY

HUBBY: "Really, Ethel, seventy-five for a hat is the height of extravagance."
WIFEY: "Well, my dear, I simply have to look nice when I'm with you. You're so distinguished looking."

Flattery and loving care have always been well-paying devices for the female.

FATHER IS GOING TO BUY A NEW MO CAR — HE DOESN'T REALIZE IT Y

DOLLY AND DOLORES

"I feel so blue this morning, I gotta wear my best dress."

"I knew from the very first you were unhappily married — your husband was altogether too polite to you."

Denys Wortman on the morale-lifting value of a pretty dress (above, left), on letting-down-the-hair (above), and on the desire to appear to be somebody *special*.

"They say he's tight, but believe me, when he goes out with me he spends."

"Now let us consider what reincarnation holds for all of us."

These cartoons of the thirties point out a weakness among some older women for the mystic and exotic, and a feminine tendency to let the mind stray from more exalted things to fashions and comparisons.

WELL, THE MEN LISTEN

*THE WOMAN WHO CONSTANTLY
REARRANGES FURNITURE MOVES
TO THE COUNTRY*

*This was the day Tomboy Taylor's mother
dropped the jar of jelly she was taking to a
sick friend.*

Three famous female peculiarities. G. B. Inwood (above, left) on the constant need for rearranging things, Fontaine Fox (above, right) on the tomboy, and J. Norman Lynd (below) on the back-seat driver.

ACCIDENT AND FIRE HAZARD

A beautiful woman can distract a man from almost anything, as Dahl of Boston shows above, and as Roy McKie has shown, right, in a series of famous advertisements for the *Ladies' Home Journal.*

y woman loves to be pampered, even
e has to do the pampering herself.

"You in here, dear?"

"Joan of Arc was a woman! Madame Curie was a woman! Sarah Bernhardt was a woman!"

Three examples of the eternal woman in co

"Now isn't it a fact that you won't listen to logic unless I make a scene?"

"So when she said that to me, merely shrugged slightly, smil in a condescending manne said I was awfully sorry she f that way about me, and haul off and hit her with my han bag."

nder Exit

Unlike men, women have few reserves about displaying their emotions in public, as Don Freeman shows us above, and Don Tobin on the lower right. Gardner Rea's hostess, on the lower left, typifies the female attitude of "making the best of things."

"*I was all out of olives, so I used clams.*"

"*Oh, mother!*"

WHEN YOU'D LOVE TO LIVE FOREVER

"Well, it isn't the ailment I had in mind, but I suppose it will do."

"Let's try it this way: each of us kick in wit[h] twenty-three cents — that makes a dollar thirty-eight, and we'll odd-man for the extra two cen[ts] — that'll take care of the meter. Then we'll tak[e] a dime out of the kitty, see? And each put i[n] two cents for the driver . . ."

"*Of course, I wouldn't say anything about her unless I could say something good, but this is really good —*"

It is rumored that some women (above and right) are talkers, and many girls (below) are burdened with a sexual inferiority complex.

"*. . . I says to her and she says to me and I says to her and she says to . . .*"

"*I know what you're doing! You're sitting there wishing I was a boy!*"

"Darling . . . you . . . you're trembling!"

Three famous clichés about the Amer
woman — the iceman (by Partch),
mother-in-law, and the teen-age crush.

"Aren't you going to say good night to mother?"

*"I am Professor Sampson, 34,
happily married, and father of
three fine children, ages . . ."*

Always the bride has a dear girl friend with a reedy little voice who sings "I Love You Truly" or "Oh Promise Me" during the cere-mony. (At the moment Lulu May is flatting all over the organ loft.)

Gossipy wedding guest. Sees all, hears all, and tells all next day, most of it wrong. How the maid of honor's slip was showing, and someone found a tack in the cake.

W. E. Hill with some pointed comments on women guests to be found at any wedding.

Wedding guest by the wedding presents ex-plaining that she wants to see what the bride needs before she selects her gift. This is the bunk, as she'll go home and dig up a pickle fork she never cared for and send that to the lucky bride.

Louise, say to your hat you're not losing, but are acquiring a hter!" Friend of the n's ma, trying to ort her but not doing ell.

Elderly relative who doesn't get out much nowadays, but just can't resist a wedding or funeral. It's a tossup which she enjoys more.

IT'S NEW . . . IT'S GOOD

Two masters of the psychological drawing, Abner Dean (above) and William Steig (right).

THIS IS HER.

PICTURE SOURCES
AND CREDITS

KEY TO SOURCE ABBREVIATIONS

u.   upper
m.   middle
b.   bottom
l.   left
r.   right
C   Collier's
GT   "The Good Things of Life," Second Series. White, Stokes & Allen, 1886

HB   Harper's Bazar
HM   Harper's Monthly
HW   Harper's Weekly
J   Judge
L   Life
PG   Police Gazette
Pic. Coll., NYPL   Picture Collection, New York Public Library

P   Puck
SEP   Saturday Evening Post
TNY   The New Yorker Magazine
UF   United Features
VF   Vanity Fair (1860-63)
VL   "Vignettes of Life," J. Norman Lynd, Reilly & Lee, 1930
YN   Yankee Notions

PICTURE CREDITS

Page
2. u., HW, Jan. 1857; b. l., YN, Aug. 1861; b. r. VF, Sept. 1862.
3. u. l., YN, July 1866; u. r., YN, Sept. 1862; b. l., YN, July 1865; b. r., YN, Jan. 1865.
4. u., HB, Aug. 1872; b. l., P, July 1878; b. r., HB, Oct. 1862.
5. u. l., J, Aug. 1882; u. r., HB, Oct. 1868; b. l., J, Feb. 1882; b. r., P, May 1877.
6. P, Apr. 1877.
7 u. l., PG; u. r., P, Feb. 1886; b., L, 1887.
8. u., "In the '400' and Out," C. J. Taylor, Keppler & Schwarzmann, 1889; b., L, Apr. 1887.
9. u., L, Vol. 26, p. 19, 1895; b., "In the '400' and Out," C. J. Taylor.
10. P, Aug. 1895.
11. u., L, Mar. 1926; l., L, Oct. 1926.
12. u., P, Aug. 1899; b. l., PG; b. r., Aug. 1900.
13. u., TNY, 1930; b. l., P, Aug. 1900; b. r., P, Feb. 1895.
14. u., "Sketches From Lowly Life," M. A. Woolf, G. P. Putnam's Sons, 1899; b., NEA Service, 1955.
15. P, Nov. 1909.
16. u., P, May 1909; b. l., P, Nov. 1908; b. r., L, Apr. 1909.
17. u., L, Apr. 1909; b., P, Mar. 1909.
18. u., J, 1913; b. l., P, June 1909; b. r., L, Mar. 1909.
19. u., J, 1913; b. l., J; b. r., J.
20. u., J; b., L, Apr. 1913.
21. u., J, Feb. 1917; b. l., L, Nov. 1920; b. r., L, Sept. 1920.
22. J, May 1917.
23. L, Feb. 1920.
24. u., J, June, 1923; b. l., L, Aug. 1924; b. r., "Cartoons from 'Life'," Ellison Hoover, Simon & Schuster, 1925.
25. L, Aug. 1924.
26. u., L, Apr. 1927; b. l., VL; b. r., L, Oct. 1925.
27. L, May 1927.
28. L, Apr. 1925.
29. u. Int'l Feature Service, 1928; b. l., L, Dec. 1928; b. r., NEA Service, 1955.
30. u., L, Jan. 1930; b., Chicago Tribune, 1930.
31. u., L, Oct. 1929; b. l., UF 1933; b. r., Chicago Tribune, 1934.
32. u., J, Apr. 1933; b., VL.
33. u., "What! More Dahl?" R. T. Hale & Co., 1944; b., Harvard Lampoon, — Jan. 1948.
34. u., "The Cartoons of Cobean," © Harper & Bros. 1952; b. l., Irwin Caplan, SEP, July 1955; b. r., Calif. Pelican, Oct. 1955.
35. u., "Dahl's Boston," Little, Brown & Co., 1946; b., SEP.
36. u., N. Y. Herald Tribune Inc. 1946; b. l., Calif. Pelican, Apr. 1951; b. r., "Keeping Women in Line," Mischa Richter, Avon.
37. u., "The Passport," Saul Steinberg, © Harper & Bros., 1954; b. l., SEP, 1955; b. r., Harvard Lampoon, Feb. 1950.
38. u., TNY, 1947.
39. u. and b., "Dahl's Brave New World," Little, Brown & Co., 1947.
40. u., Bell Syndicate, Sept. 1953; b. l., Reprinted from THIS WEEK Magazine, © 1954 by the United Newspapers Magazine Corp.; b. r., SEP, Feb. 1956.

Page
41. Reprinted by permission from "Ever Since Adam and Eve," edited by Alfred Andriola and Mel Casson, published by McGraw-Hill Book Company, Inc. Copyright 1955, Alfred Andriola and Mel Casson.
44. u., YN, Feb. 1862; b., YN, Oct. 1863.
45. u., HB, Mar. 1872; b., HB, Dec. 1872.
46. u., GT; b., P, July 1886.
47. L, vol. 17, p. 318, 1890.
48, 49. u., L, 1892; b., L, Aug. 1893.
50. P, Dec. 1895.
51. u., Pic. Coll., NYPL; b., GT.
52. u., "The Social Comedy," Life Publishing Co., 1902; b., P, Feb. 1900.
53. u., P, Apr. 1900; b., P, Mar. 1900.
54. u., NEA Service; b., P, July 1908.
55. u., N. Y. Tribune Inc., 1928; b., same, 1927.
56. u., J, 1917; b., P, May 1917.
57. u., L, Mar. 1928; b., L, Mar. 1927.
58. u., L, Feb. 1927; b. l., VL; b. r., L, Nov. 1932.
59. u., UF, 1939; l., UF.
60. u., C, Aug. 1941; b., "Man About Town," Long & Smith, 1932.
61. u., TNY, 1939; b., C, 1942.
62. u. l., Reprinted by permission from "Ever Since Adam and Eve," edited by Alfred Andriola and Mel Casson, published by McGraw-Hill Book Company. Copyright 1955, Alfred Andriola and Mel Casson. u.r., SEP, 1955; b.l., Cornell Widow Scrapbook 1950; b. r., Kate Osann, C, 1951.
63. Reprinted by permission from "Ever Since Adam and Eve," edited by Alfred Andriola and Mel Casson, published by McGraw-Hill Book Company, Inc. Copyright 1955, Alfred Andriola and Mel Casson.
64. u., "Cave Drawings for the Future," Dial 1954; b., "Cartoon Laughs," Fawcett Publications.
66. u., VF, Dec. 1860; b., P, July 1878.
67. u., "Stuff and Nonsense," A. B. Frost, Scribner's, 1888; b., L, p. 162, 1887.
68. u., P, Jan. 1900; b., P, May 1895.
69. u., P, Oct. 1900; b., P, June 1895.
70. u. l., P, Sept. 1900; u. r., "The Social Comedy," Life Pub. Co. 1902; b. l., L, Aug. 1926.
71. u., P, Mar. 1900; b., P, Aug. 1900.
72. u., P, Aug. 1900; b., L, Apr. 1906.
73. u., P, July 1902; b., P, May 1902.
74. u., P, June 1909; b., P, Nov. 1909.
75. L, July 1917.
76. u. l., L, Mar. 1928; u. r., L, Sept. 1920; b., VL.
77. u., "This One's on Me," M. Richter, McGraw-Hill, 1945; b. l., C, 1945; b. r., SEP, 1952.
78. u., TNY, 1951; b., NEA Service, 1954.
79. u., John Hart, True: the Man's Magazine, 1955; b., Walt Wetterberg, American Magazine, 1953.
80. u., TNY, 1954; b., From Sports Illustrated, © Mar. 1955, Time Inc.
81. u., From Sports Illustrated, © Apr. 1956, Time Inc.; b., C, Mar. 1947.
84. u., Pic. Coll., NYPL; b., HM, Sept. 1852.
85. u., HW, 1859; b., Currier & Ives, 1869.
86. HB, Jan. 1869.

Page

87. u., Print Room, NYPL; b. l., HB, Nov. 1874; b. r., PG, 1882.
88. P, Dec. 1895.
89. u. & b., L, 1896.
90. L, Mar. 1897.
91. u., L, Vol. 27, p. 58-59, 1896; b., P, May 1900.
92. u., L, vol. 27, 1896; b. l., PG, Mar. 1883; b. r., "The Social Comedy," Life Publishing Co., 1902.
93. u., P, May 1900; b., P, Apr. 1908.
94, 95. P, Mar. 1908.
96. u., J, 1912; b. l., L, Sept. 1915; b. r., J, 1913.
97. u., J, 1915; b., L, Sept. 1913.
98. u., "Memorial Edition, Clare Briggs," Wise, 1930; b., NEA Service, 1930.
99. u., L, Jan. 1915; b., P, May 1917.
100. u., J, Aug. 1917; b., P, Aug. 1917.
101. u., L, July 1917; b. l., P, Aug. 1917; b. r., P, Apr. 1917.
102. u., P, Apr. 1917; b. L, July 1920.
103. u., L, Dec. 1920; b., L, Aug. 1920.
104. u. & b., L, Oct. 1924.
105. L, June 1925.
106. u., L, Dec. 1926; b., "The Best of Art Young," Vanguard, 1936.
107. u., L, Mar. 1930; b., L, Nov. 1929.
108. u., L, Dec. 1930; b. l., L, Sept. 1930; b. r., UF.
109. u., UF, Apr. 1937; b., TNY, 1933.
110. u., N. Y. Herald Tribune Inc., 1942; b., C, 1945.
111. u. l. & r., C, 1942; b., "What! More Dahl?" R. T. Hale & Co., 1944.
112. u., TNY, 1934; b., TNY, 1947.
113. u., Anne Cleveland, "Vassar, A Second Glance," The Vassar Cooperative Bookshop; b., N. Y. Herald Tribune, Dec. 1947.
114. u., Reprinted by permission from "Ever Since Adam and Eve," edited by Alfred Andriola and Mel Casson, published by McGraw-Hill Book Company, Inc. Copyright 1955, Alfred Andriola and Mel Casson; b. l., SEP, 1955; b. r., Look, Jan. 1956.
115. "The Cartoons of Cobean," © Harper & Bros., 1952; b. l., SEP, 1950; b. r., SEP, Dec. 1955.
116. u., C, 1946; b. l. & r., The Chicago Tribune-N. Y. News Syndicate, May 1955.
117. u., "This One's on Me," McGraw-Hill, 1945; b. l., "Best Cartoons from True," Fawcett, 1955; b. r., Saturday Review, Nov. 1953.
118. The Chicago Tribune-N. Y. News Syndicate, Oct. 1955.
120. u. l., P, Aug. 1877; u. r., P, May, 1878; b., June 1880.
121. u., P, Aug. 1900; b., GT.
122. u., GT; b. l., P, Feb. 1900; b. r., GT.
123. u., "The Social Comedy," Life Publishing Co., 1902; b., P, Sept. 1892.
124. u. l., The Chicago Tribune, 1929; u. r., NEA Service, 1954; b., L, Apr. 1898.
125. u., L, Oct. 1926; b. l., NEA Service; b. r., NEA Service, 1954.
126. u., P, Feb. 1902; b., P, Aug. 1907.
127. u., J, 1913; m., J, 1916; b., P, Aug. 1917.
128. From Vanity Fair, © 1921, The Condé Nast Publications Inc.; b. l., J, Dec. 1923; b. r., P, Apr. 1917.
129. u., L, Apr. 1927; b., L, Feb. 1926.
130. u., "The Best of Art Young," Vanguard, 1936; b., L, Aug. 1926.
131. u., Liberty, Feb. 1932; b., Reprinted by permission Ladies' Home Journal, Oct. 1927.
132. u., L, July 1928; b. l., L, Sept. 1930; b. r., Ballyhoo, Aug. 1936.
133. u., TNY, 1930; b., TNY, 1939.
134. TNY, 1947.
135. u. l., Pennpix, Oct. 1953; u. r., NEA Service 1952; b., "Dahl's Brave New World," Little, Brown & Co., 1947.
136. u., N. Y. Herald Tribune Inc., 1954; b., Saturday Review, May 1956.
138. u., HB, Dec. 1868; b., P, Feb. 1886.
139. u., P, Jan. 1889; b., HB, Jan. 1868.
140. u., P, Sept. 1877; b., P, May 1880.
141. P, Oct. 1883.
142. u. & b., GT.
143. u., P, Oct. 1885; b., P, Apr. 1886.
144. u., "In the '400' and Out," C. J. Taylor, Keppler & Schwarzmann, 1889; b. l., P, Nov. 1892; b. r., P, Mar. 1892.

145. u., L, 1893; b., "The Social Comedy," Life Publishing Co., 1902.
146. u., L, 1900; b., P, Aug. 1894.
147. u., L, Feb. 1907; b. l., NEA Service, 1939; b. r., P, May 1908.
148. u., P, Aug. 1908; b., P, July 1900.
149. u. & b., "The Social Comedy," Life Publishing Co., 1902.
150. u. & b., P, Sept. 1909.
151. u. & b., "Oh, Man!" P. F. Volland & Co., 1919
152. u., VL; b., J, 1912.
153. u., "The Selected Drawings of Clare Briggs," Wise, 1930; b., P, Aug. 1908.
154. u., N. Y. Herald Tribune, 1930; b., "The Selected Drawings of Clare Briggs," Wise, 1930.
155. L, Dec. 1930.
156. u., UF, 1933; b., UF.
157. u., "The Best of Art Young," Vanguard, 1936; b., TNY, 1934.
158. u., TNY, 1928; b., C, 1943.
159. u., "The Coffee Break," Dutton's, 1955; m., SEP, 1955; b., Berenstains, "Marital Blitz," Dell, 1955.
160. TNY, 1933.
161. u., "Man About Town," Long & Smith, 1932; b., The New York Times Book Review, Feb. 1948.
162. u., The New York Times Book Review, May 1951; b. l., C, 1946; b. r., NEA Service, 1938.
163. u., "Funny Cartoons," Fawcett, 1954; b. l., SEP, 1947; b. r., "Juvenile Delinquency," Dell, 1956.
164. u., TNY, 1935; b., Reprinted by permission from "Ever Since Adam and Eve," edited by Alfred Andriola and Mel Casson, published by McGraw-Hill Book Company, Inc. Copyright 1955, Alfred Andriola and Mel Casson.
165. u., "Homes of the Brave," by T. H. Robsjohn-Gibbings © Knopf, 1954; b., SEP, 1952.
166. u., C, Apr. 1941; b., Village Voice, Apr. 1956.
167. u., NEA Service, 1954; b., SEP.
168. u., TNY, 1940; b., "Cartoon Laughs," Fawcett Publications.
169. TNY, 1953.
172. u., P, May 1877; b. l., HB, 1874; b. r., HB, Nov. 1874.
173. u., P, Mar. 1878; b., P, Nov. 1883.
174. u., L, vol. 22, 1893; b., P, Aug. 1895.
175. u. L, 1897; b., P, Apr. 1900.
176. l., P, Dec. 1900; r., "Funny Folks," Dutton's, 1899.
177. u. l., Eve. Journal, 1907; u. r., P, Aug. 1908; b., P, Mar. 1902.
178. u. & b., J, 1915.
179. u., & b., J, Ma. 1917.
180-181. From Vanity Fair, © 1917, The Condé Nast Publications, Inc.
182. "Oh, Man!" P. F. Volland & Co., 1919.
183. L, Aug. 1920.
184. u., L, Sept. 1920; b., L, Nov. 1920.
185. u. l., UF, 1938; u. r., UF, 1939; b., UF.
186. u., L, Aug. 1931; b., VL.
187. u. l., L, Aug. 1931; u. r., Bell Syndicate, 1918; b., VL.
188. u., "Dahl's Brave New World," Little Brown & Co., 1947; b., Reprinted by permission Ladies Home Journal, May 1954.
189. u., "This One's on Me," McGraw-Hill, 1945; b., Corka, © Nation's Business, July 1952.
190. u., C, July 1941; b. l., Reprinted by permission from "Ever Since Adam and Eve," edited by Alfred Andriola and Mel Casson, published by McGraw-Hill Book Company, Inc. Copyright 1955, Alfred Andriola and Mel Casson; b. r., SEP, Feb. 1956.
191. u., "Don Freeman's Newsstand," Sept. 1936; b. l., "Cartoon Fun," Fawcett, 1954; b. r., SEP, Jan. 1956.
192. u., NEA Service, 1953; b. l., SEP, Aug. 1955; b. r., SEP, 1954.
193. u., SEP, 1951; m., SEP, 1950; b., C, 1955.
194. u., "Funny Cartoons," Fawcett, 1954; b. l., SEP, Oct. 1955; b. r., C, Sept. 1955.
195. The Chicago Tribune-N. Y. News Syndicate, June 1956.
196. u., "And on the Eighth Day," Simon & Schuster, 1949; b., "The Rejected Lovers," by William Steig, © Knopf, 1951.

INDEX